Geography Alive!

Regions and People

Interactive Student Notebook

Teachers' Curriculum Institute

Director of Development: Liz Russell

Editorial Project Manager: Laura Alavosus

Content Editors: John Bergez, John Burner

Production Editors: Mali Apple, Beverly Cory

Editorial Assistant: Anna Embree

Art Director: John F. Kelly

Production Manager: Lynn Sanchez

Senior Graphic Designer: Christy Uyeno

Graphic Designers: Katy Haun, Paul Rebello, Don Taka

Photo Edit Manager: Margee Robinson

Art Editor: Eric Houts

Audio Director: Katy Haun

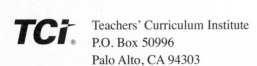

Teachers' Curriculum Institute
P.O. Box 50996
Palo Alto, CA 94303

ISBN13: 978-1-58371-433-1   ISBN10: ISBN 1-58371-433-2
5 6 7 8 9 10 -DH- 12 11 10 09 08

Program Directors
Bert Bower
Jim Lobdell

Program Advisors
National Council for
Geographic Education

Curriculum Developers
Julie Cremin
Erin Fry
Amy George
Colleen Guccione
Steve Seely
Kelly Shafsky
Lisa Sutterer

Author
Diane Hart

Contributing Writers
Wendy Frey
Erin Fry
Brent Goff
Holly Melton
Hilarie Staton
Ellen Todras
Julie Weiss

Teacher and Content Consultants
Melissa Aubuchon
    Indian Trail Middle School
    Plainfield Community Consolidated
        School District 202
    Plainfield, Illinois

Jim Bredin
    Office of the Great Lakes
    Lansing, Michigan

Srinivasan Damodharan
    New Horizon High School
    Bangalore, India

Sarah Giese
    Kenmore Middle School
    Arlington Public Schools
    Arlington, Virginia

Jim Gindling
    Willink Middle School
    Webster Central School District
    Webster, New York

Diana Jordan
    Kenmore Middle School
    Arlington Public Schools
    Arlington, Virginia

Marianne Kenney (NCGE)
    Geography Education Consultant
    Denver, Colorado

Miles Lawrence
    NOAA TPC/National Hurricane
        Center
    Miami, Florida

Patrick McCrystle
    Bellarmine College Preparatory
    San Jose, California

Deanna Morrow
    Martinez Middle School
    Hillsborough County School District
    Lutz, Florida

Michael Radcliffe
    Greenville High School
    Greenville Public Schools
    Greenville, Michigan

Betsy Sheffield
    National Snow and Ice Data Center
    Boulder, Colorado

Stacy Stewart
    NOAA TPC/National Hurricane
        Center
    Miami, Florida

Fred Walk (NCGE)
    Normal Community High School
    McLean County Unit District No. 5
    Normal, Illinois

    Department of Geography
    Illinois State University
    Normal, Illinois

Scholars
Dr. Siaw Akwawua
    College of Humanities and
        Social Sciences
    University of Northern Colorado

Dr. Robert Bednarz (NCGE)
    College of Geosciences
    Texas A&M University

Dr. James Dunn (NCGE)
    College of Humanities and
        Social Sciences
    University of Northern Colorado

Dr. Bill Fraser
    Biology Department
    Montana State University

Dr. Patricia Gober (NCGE)
    Department of Geography
    Arizona State University

Dr. Susan Hardwick (NCGE)
Department of Geography
University of Oregon

Professor Gail Hobbs (NCGE)
Department of Anthropological
and Geographical Sciences
Los Angeles Pierce College

Dr. Phil Klein (NCGE)
College of Humanities and
Social Sciences
University of Northern Colorado

Dr. Gwenda Rice (NCGE)
College of Education
Western Oregon University

Dr. Kit Salter (retired; NCGE)
Department of Geography
University of Missouri

Dr. Earl Scott (retired)
Department of Geography
University of Minnesota

Music Consultant
Melanie Pinkert
Music Faculty
Montgomery College, Maryland

Geography Specialist
Mapping Specialists
Madison, Wisconsin

Internet Consultant
Clinton Couse
Educational Technology Consultant
Seattle, Washington

Researcher
Jessica Efron
Library Faculty
Appalachian State University

Contents

Unit 1   The Geographer's World

Lesson 1   The Tools of Geography
Geoterms   4
Reading Notes   5
Processing   11

Lesson 2   Seeing the World Like a Geographer
Preview   12
Geoterms   13
Reading Notes   15
Processing   21

Unit 2   Canada and the United States

Lesson 3   Settlement Patterns and Ways of Life in Canada
Geoterms   25
Reading Notes   26
Processing   28

Lesson 4   The Great Lakes: The U.S. and Canada's Freshwater Treasures
Preview   30
Geoterms   32
Reading Notes   33

Lesson 5   Urban Sprawl in North America: Where Will It End?
Preview   36
Geoterms   37
Reading Notes   38
Processing   44

Lesson 6   National Parks: Saving the Natural Heritage of the U.S. and Canada
Preview   46
Geoterms   47
Reading Notes   48
Processing   56

Lesson 7   Consumption Patterns in the United States: The Impact of Living Well
Geoterms   58
Reading Notes   59
Processing   63

Lesson 8   Migration to the United States: The Impact on People and Places
Preview   64
Geoterms   66
Reading Notes   67
Processing   69

Unit 3   Latin America

Lesson 9   Spatial Inequality in Mexico City: From Cardboard to Castles
Preview   72
Geoterms   73
Reading Notes   74

Lesson 10   Indigenous Cultures: The Survival of the Maya of Mesoamerica
Preview   78
Geoterms   79
Reading Notes   80
Processing   82

Lesson 11 **Dealing with Extreme Weather: Hurricanes in the Caribbean**
Preview   84
Geoterms   85
Reading Notes   86
Processing   88

Lesson 12 **Land Use Conflict in the Amazon Rainforest**
Preview   90
Geoterms   91
Reading Notes   92
Processing   95

Lesson 13 **Life in the Central Andes: Adapting to a Mountainous Region**
Preview   96
Geoterms   97
Reading Notes   98
Processing   100

Unit 4 **Europe and Russia**

Lesson 14 **Supranational Cooperation in the European Union**
Preview   104
Geoterms   105
Reading Notes   106
Processing   109

Lesson 15 **Population Dilemmas in Europe**
Preview   110
Geoterms   111
Reading Notes   112
Processing   115

Lesson 16 **Invisible Borders: Transboundary Pollution in Europe**
Geoterms   117
Reading Notes   118
Processing   121

Lesson 17 **Russia's Varied Landscape: Physical Processes at Work**
Preview   122
Geoterms   123
Reading Notes   124
Processing   128

Lesson 18 **New Nation-States from the Old Soviet Empire: Will They Succeed?**
Preview   130
Geoterms   131
Reading Notes   132

Unit 5 **Africa**

Lesson 19 **The Nile River: A Journey from Source to Mouth**
Preview   140
Geoterms   141
Reading Notes   142
Processing   146

Lesson 20 **Life in the Sahara and the Sahel: Adapting to a Desert Region**
Preview   148
Geoterms   149
Reading Notes   150
Processing   152

Lesson 21 **Micro-entrepreneurs: Women's Role in the Development of Africa**
Preview   154
Geoterms   155
Reading Notes   156

**Lesson 22 Nigeria: A Country of
Many Cultures**
Preview   158
Geoterms   159
Reading Notes   160
Processing   162

**Lesson 23 Resources and Power in
Post-apartheid South Africa**
Preview   164
Geoterms   165
Reading Notes   166
Processing   170

Unit 6   Southwest and
Central Asia

**Lesson 24 Oil in Southwest Asia:
How "Black Gold" Has Shaped
a Region**
Preview   174
Geoterms   175
Reading Notes   176
Processing   179

**Lesson 25 Istanbul: A Primate City
Throughout History**
Geoterms   181
Reading Notes   182
Processing   184

**Lesson 26 The Aral Sea: Central Asia's
Shrinking Water Source**
Preview   186
Geoterms   187
Reading Notes   188
Processing   190

Unit 7   Monsoon Asia

**Lesson 27 Waiting for the Rains:
The Effects of Monsoons
in South Asia**
Preview   194
Geoterms   195
Reading Notes   196
Processing   200

**Lesson 28 Tech Workers and Time Zones:
India's Comparative Advantage**
Preview   202
Geoterms   204
Reading Notes   205

**Lesson 29 Mount Everest: Climbing the
World's Tallest Physical Feature**
Preview   208
Geoterms   209
Reading Notes   210
Processing   214

**Lesson 30 China: The World's Most
Populous Country**
Geoterms   216
Reading Notes   217
Processing   220

**Lesson 31 Population Density in Japan:
Life in a Crowded Country**
Preview   222
Geoterms   223
Reading Notes   224
Processing   226

**Lesson 32 The Global Sneaker:
From Asia to Everywhere**
Preview   228
Geoterms   229
Reading Notes   230
Processing   232

Unit 8   Oceania and Antarctica

**Lesson 33   Relative and Absolute Location:
What Makes Australia Unique?**
Preview   237
Geoterms   238
Reading Notes   239
Processing   242

**Lesson 34   The Pacific Islands: Adapting
to Life Surrounded by Ocean**
Preview   244
Geoterms   245
Reading Notes   246
Processing   250

**Lesson 35   Antarctica: Researching Global
Warming at the Coldest Place
on Earth**
Preview   252
Geoterms   253
Reading Notes   254

Regions of the World

Within the map:
- **CANADA AND THE UNITED STATES**
- *ATLANTIC OCEAN*
- *PACIFIC OCEAN*
- **LATIN AMERICA**

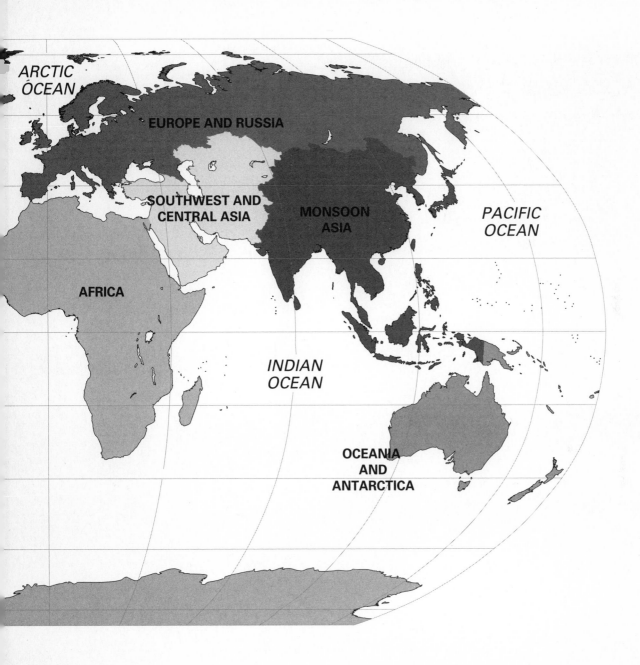

ARCTIC
OCEAN

EUROPE AND RUSSIA

SOUTHWEST AND
CENTRAL ASIA

MONSOON
ASIA

PACIFIC
OCEAN

AFRICA

INDIAN
OCEAN

OCEANIA
AND
ANTARCTICA

Read Sections 1.1 and 1.2. Then create an illustrated dictionary of the
Geoterms by completing these tasks:

- Create a symbol or an illustration to represent each Geoterm.
- Write a definition of each term in your own words.
- Write a sentence that includes the Geoterm and the word *map*.

Geoterm and Symbol	Definition	Sentence
absolute location		
distortion		
map projection		
relative location		

1.3 Map Titles and Symbols

Label the map. Follow the directions on the cards your teacher gives you.

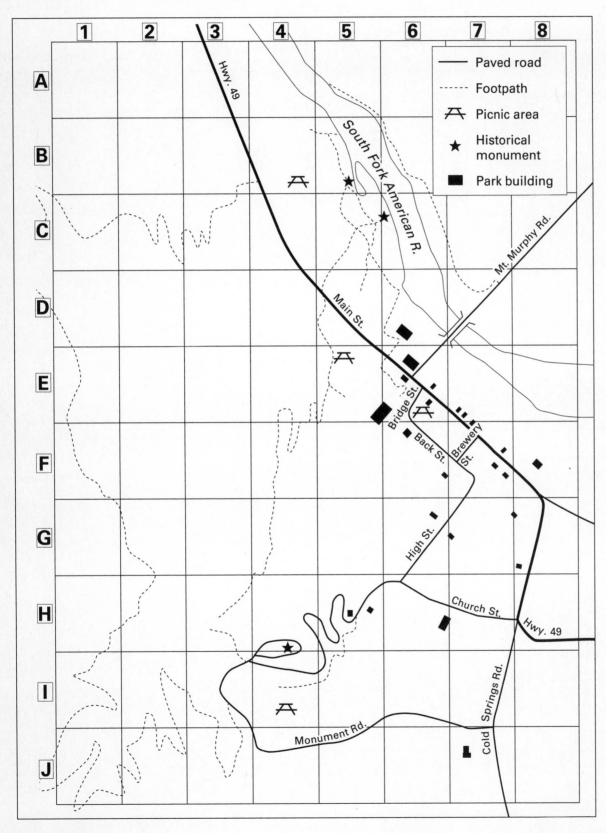

1.4 The Global Grid: Longitude and Latitude

Label the map. Follow the directions on the cards your teacher gives you.

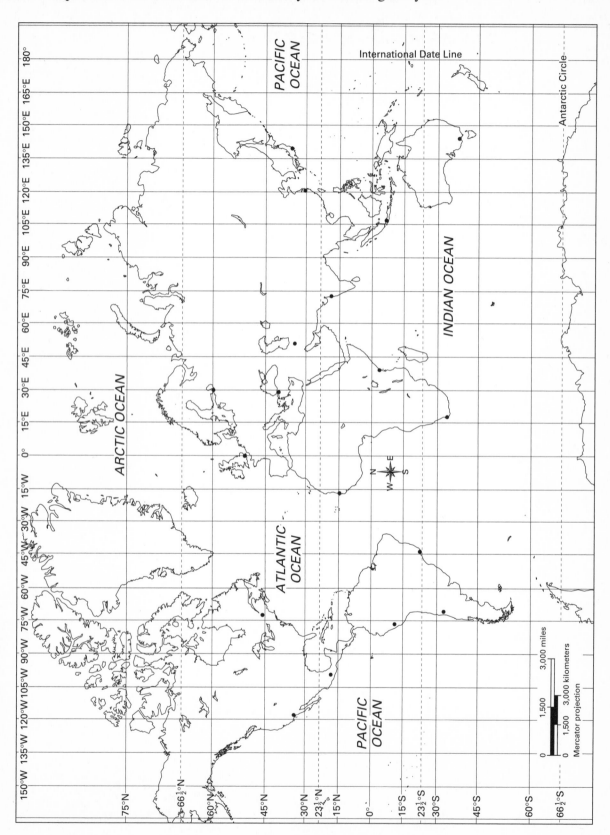

Cities Around the World

1.5 Dealing with Distances: Map Scale

Label the maps. Follow the directions on the cards your teacher gives you.

Washington, D.C., and Surrounding Areas

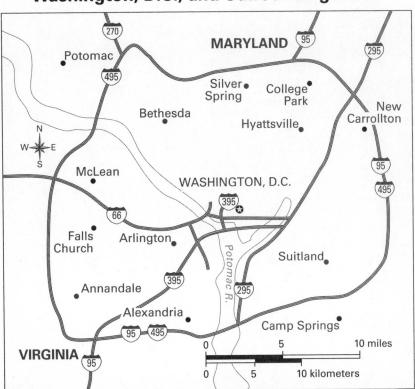

Downtown Washington, D.C.

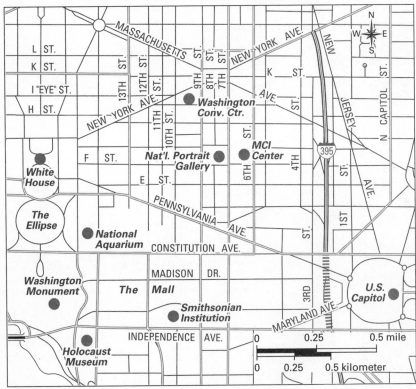

1.6 Hemispheres, Continents, and Oceans

Label the map. Follow the directions on the cards your teacher gives you.

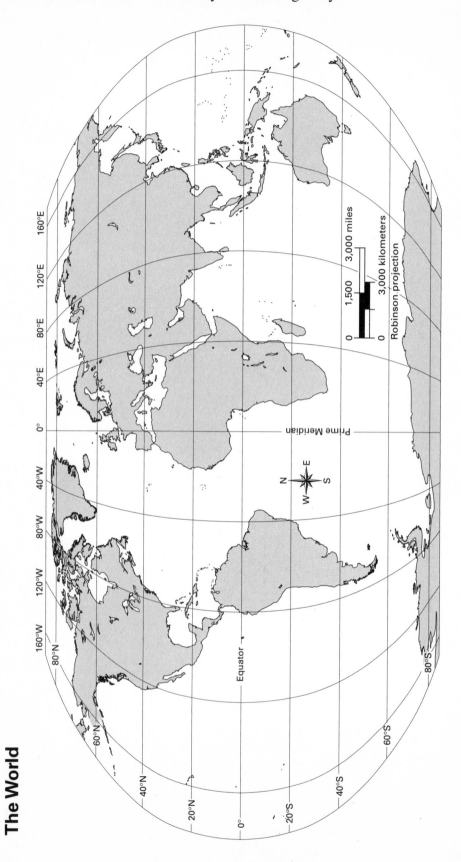

The World

1.7 Earth and the Sun

Label the map. Follow the directions on the cards your teacher gives you.

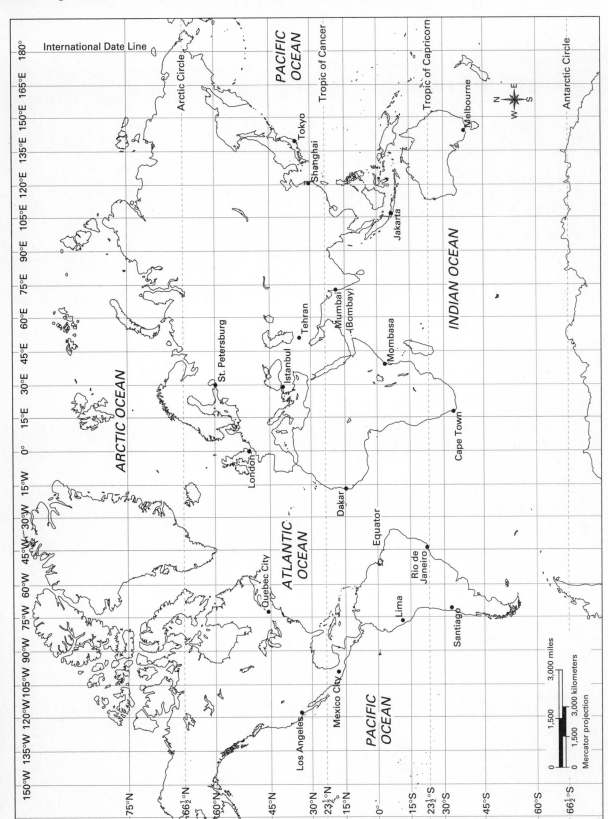

Cities Around the World

1.8 Showing a Round World on a Flat Map

Label the maps. Follow the directions on the cards your teacher gives you.

The World

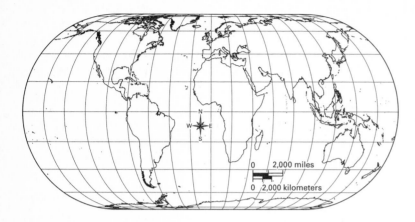

The World

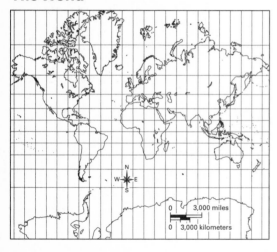

The World

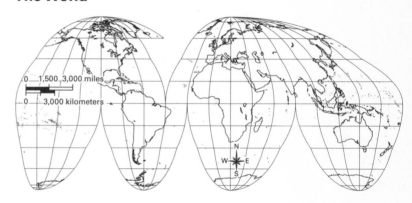

The World

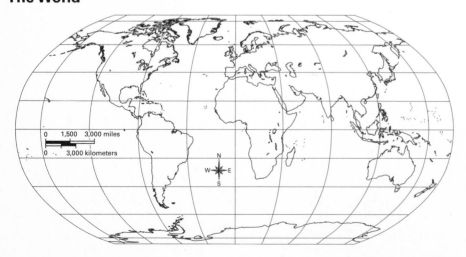

In the space below, create a map of your classroom. Include these things on your map:

- an appropriate title
- a legend with symbols that represent the furniture and other objects in the room
- a compass rose
- a grid
- an accurate scale

Design an advertisement that encourages people to move to your town or city. Include these things in your ad:

- a memorable slogan
- a map that shows where your town or city is located in your state
- an illustration and brief caption for each of the following: landscape, average weather conditions, plant life, the estimated number of people living in your town or city, jobs
- creative touches to make the ad eye-catching and attractive
- writing that has correct grammar and spelling

Read Sections 2.1 and 2.2. Then create an illustrated dictionary of the
Geoterms by completing these tasks:

- Create a symbol or an illustration to represent each term.
- Write a definition of each term in your own words.
- Write a sentence that includes the term and the word *map*.

Geoterm and Symbol	Definition	Sentence
climate		
economic activity		
landform		
physical feature		

GEOTERMS 2

Geoterm and Symbol	Definition	Sentence
population density		
region		
thematic map		
vegetation		

Read Section 2.3. Write one or two sentences describing the type of thematic map you read about. Then match the physical features in the Word Bank to their correct locations on the illustration. An example is done for you.

2.3 Mapping Earth's Physical Features

A world physical features map shows information about

_____

_____

Physical Features

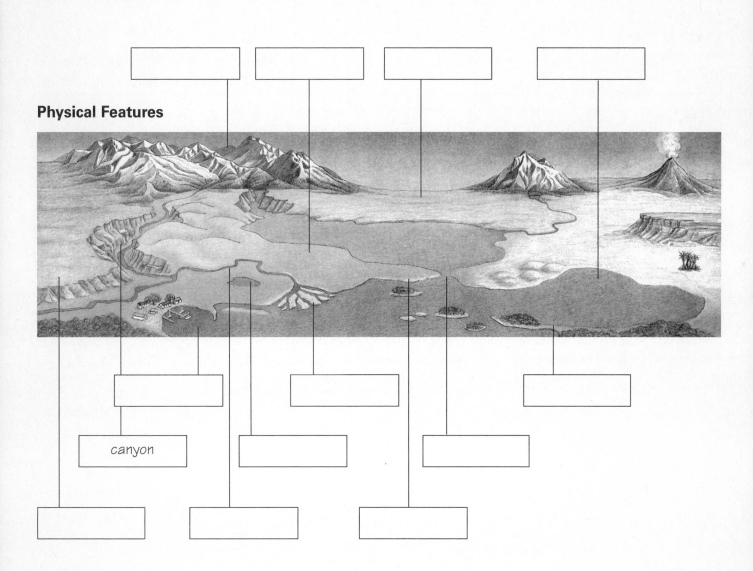

canyon

Word Bank: basin   bay   delta   gulf   isthmus   lake

mountain   peninsula   plain   plateau   river   strait
range

Read Section 2.4. Write one or two sentences describing the type of thematic map you read about. Then complete the list of climate zones by filling in the missing pieces. Each entry should have a key term, an icon, and a definition.

2.4 Hot, Cold, Wet, Dry: Earth's Climates

A world climate map shows information about

_____

_____

Climate Zones

ice cap: very cold all year with permanent ice and snow

Mediterranean: warm all year with dry summers and short, rainy winters

tundra:

arid: hot and dry all year with very little rain

_____: cold, snowy winters and cool, rainy summers

semiarid:

marine west coast: warm summers, cool winters, and rainfall all year

_____: hot all year with rainy and dry seasons

_____: warm, rainy summers and cool, snowy winters

tropical wet:

_____: hot, rainy summers and mild winters with some rain

highlands:

Read Section 2.5. Write one or two sentences describing the type of thematic map you read about. Then complete the list of vegetation zones by filling in the missing pieces. Each entry should have a key term, an icon, and a definition.

2.5 Trees and Other Plants: Earth's Vegetation

A world vegetation map shows information about

_____

_____

Vegetation Zones

ice cap:

_____: small trees and bushes adapted to a Mediterranean climate

tundra: treeless plain with grasses, mosses, and scrubs adapted to a cold climate

_____: trees with broad, flat leaves that are shed before winter

desert: arid region with few plants

_____: a mix of coniferous and deciduous trees

desert scrub:

coniferous forest:

temperate grassland:

broadleaf evergreen forest: tall trees with large leaves that remain green all year

_____: grasses and scattered trees adapted to a tropical wet and dry climate

highlands: vegetation varies with latitude and elevation

Read Section 2.6. Write one or two sentences describing the type of thematic map you read about. Then complete the list of population densities by filling in the missing pieces. Each entry should have a key term, an icon, and a definition.

2.6 Where People Live: Population Density

A world population density map shows information about

_____

_____

Population Density

more than 250 people per square mile: an average of more than 250 people live in every square mile

125–250 people per square mile:

_____: an average of 25 to 125 people live in every square mile

_____: an average of 2 to 25 people live in every square mile

fewer than 2 people per square mile:

Read Section 2.7. Write one or two sentences describing the type of thematic map you read about. Then complete the list of economic activities by filling in the missing pieces. Each entry should have a key term, an icon, and a definition.

2.7 Economic Activity: Land and Resources

A world economic activity map shows information about

_____

_____

Economic Activity

hunting and gathering: people hunt animals and gather plants for their food

_____: using trees to make homes, furniture, and paper

subsistence farming:

trade and manufacturing: buying and selling goods; turning natural resources into things to sell

_____: farmers raise crops or livestock to sell

nomadic herding:

livestock raising:

commercial fishing: catching fish in oceans, lakes, and rivers

Read Section 2.8. Write one or two sentences describing the type of thematic map you read about. Then color and label each of the seven world regions.

2.8 Organizing Earth's Surface: Regions

A world regions map shows information about

_____

_____

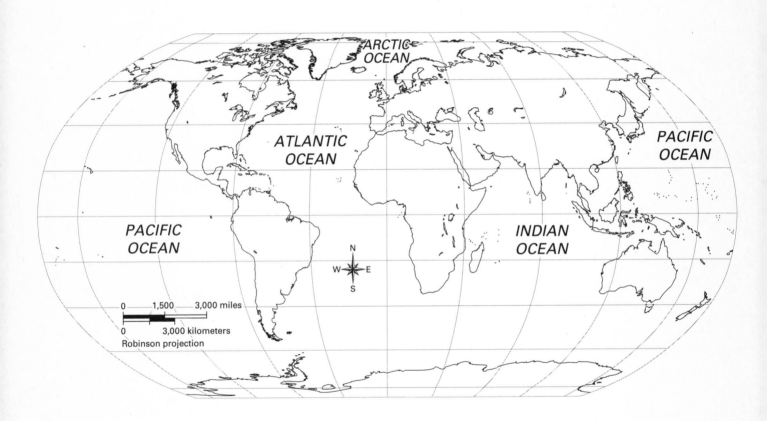

Create a seven-line poem about a country of your choice. Choose any country you like. Follow the format given below to write your poem. Use all six thematic maps in Chapter 2 to help you.

Line 1 Country name

Line 2 One physical feature located in your country

Line 3 Two adjectives describing your country's climate

Line 4 One detail about your country's vegetation

Line 5 Two adjectives describing your country's population density

Line 6 One detail about land use or resources in your country

Line 7 Region name

Add colorful and creative touches to decorate your poem.

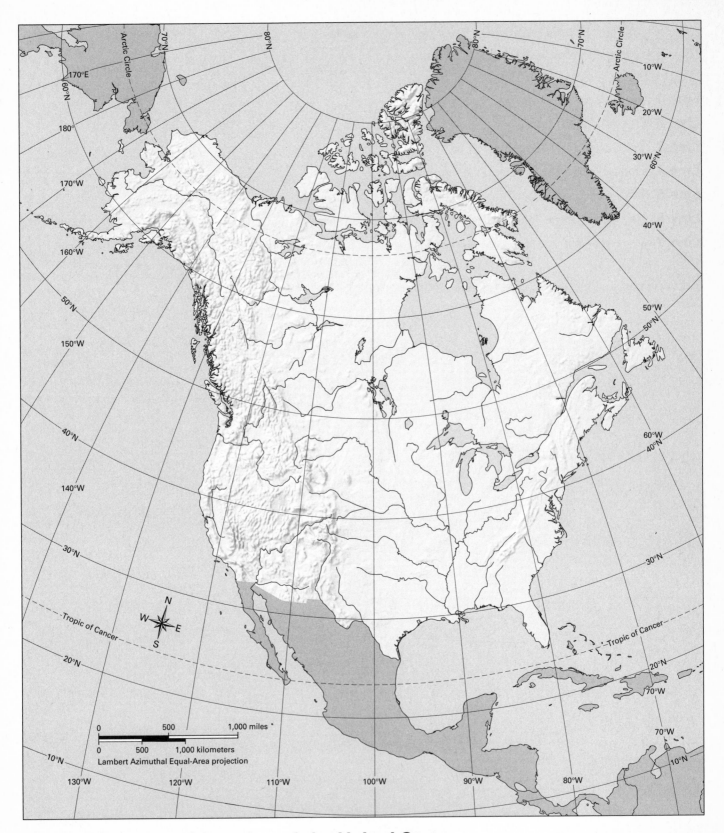

Physical Features of Canada and the United States

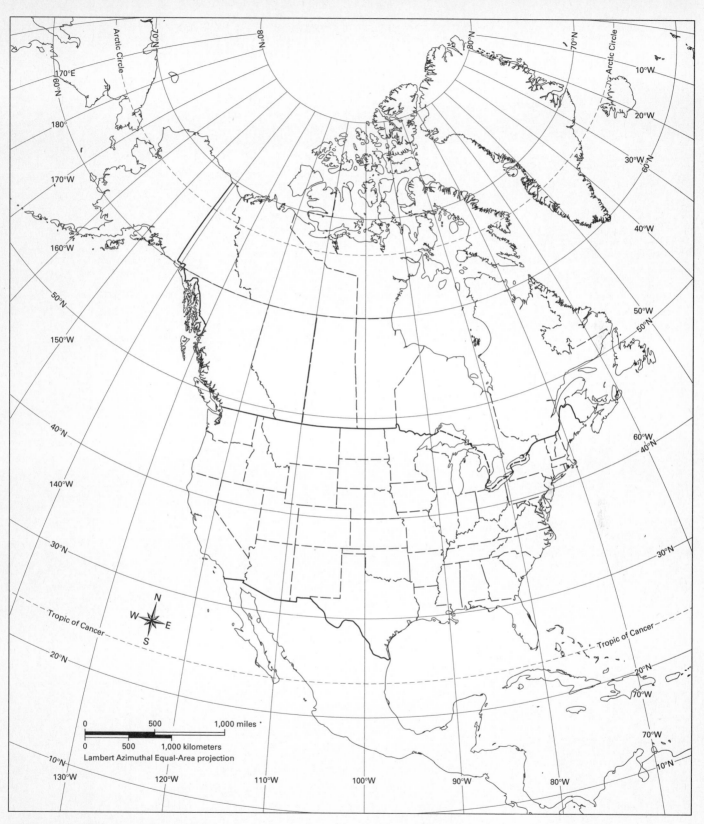

Political Boundaries of Canada and the United States

Read Sections 3.1 and 3.2. Then create an illustrated dictionary of the
Geoterms by completing these tasks:

- Create a symbol or an illustration to represent each term.
- Write a definition of each term in your own words.
- Write a sentence that includes the term and the word *Canada*.

Geoterm and Symbol	Definition	Sentence
ecumene		
plural society		
rural		
urban		

Take notes after each round of the game. Follow these directions:

1. Read the section of your book on that topic.
2. For each of Canada's five regions, record two or more key aspects of life you learned about that topic.

Pacific Region

Population:

Language:

Climate:

Buildings:

Economic activity:

Northern Region

Population:

Language:

Climate:

The Five Regions of Canada

Prairie Region

Population:

Language:

Climate:

Buildings:

Economic activity:

© Teachers' Curriculum Institute

Buildings:

Economic activity:

Atlantic Region

Population:

Language:

Climate:

Buildings:

Economic activity:

Core Region

Population:

Language:

Climate:

Buildings:

Economic activity:

Think of three examples that show how where you live influences how you live. For example, if you live near mountains, you might go skiing or snowboarding in the winter.

Draw an outline of your state. Locate and label your community. Then, on your map, illustrate your three examples.

Talk about these questions with your partner. Then write your answers.

• Which is the largest of the Great Lakes?

• Which is the smallest of the Great Lakes?

• How many U.S. states and Canadian provinces border the Great Lakes?

• Which country controls more of the Great Lakes: the United States or Canada?

• What is the approximate distance from the southern end of the St. Lawrence River to Duluth, Minnesota?

The Great Lakes Region

Talk about these questions with your partner. Then write your answers.

• Which Great Lake is the deepest?

• Which Great Lake is the shallowest?

• Why does water flow from Lake Superior into the St. Lawrence River and out to the Atlantic?

• Which lake do you think people could pollute most quickly? Why?

Profile of the Great Lakes

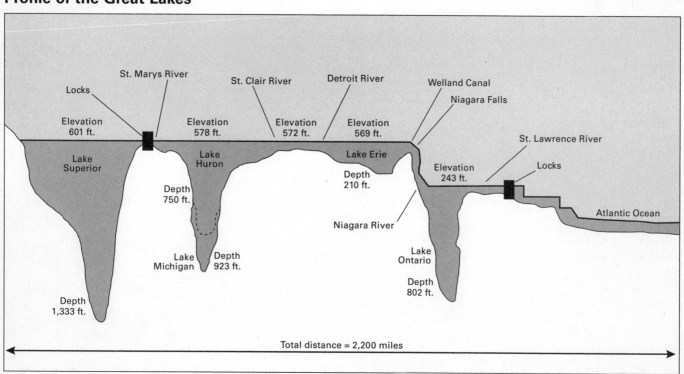

Read Sections 4.1 and 4.2. Then create an illustrated dictionary of the
Geoterms by completing these tasks:

- Create a symbol or an illustration to represent each term.
- Write a definition of each term in your own words.
- Write a sentence that includes the term and the words *Great Lakes*.

Geoterm and Symbol	Definition	Sentence
ecosystem		
food chain		
food web		
freshwater		
watershed		

Pollution in the Great Lakes Ecosystem

Read Section 4.4. Then follow the steps below.

1. On the diagram, draw and label these things:

   • two examples of point-source pollution

   • one example of non-point-source pollution

   • two ways that pollution is still a problem in the Great Lakes

2. List positive and negative information from your book and the matching station in the room.

Positive Signs	Negative Signs

Invasive Species in the Great Lakes Ecosystem

Read Section 4.5. Then follow the steps below.

1. On the diagram, draw and label these things:

   • one way invasive species enter the Great Lakes

   • two examples of invasive species

   • two solutions to the invasive species problem

2. List positive and negative information from your book and the
   matching station in the room.

Positive Signs	Negative Signs

Habitat Loss in the Great Lakes Ecosystem

Read Section 4.6. Then follow the steps below.

1. On the diagram, draw and label these things:
   • two ways habitat was lost
   • two ways habitat has been restored or protected

2. List positive and negative information from your book and the matching station in the room.

Positive Signs	**Negative Signs**

Look at the two maps of Phoenix that your teacher is projecting. With your partner, brainstorm how this community might be affected as it grows larger.

In each box below, write one way that part of the community might be affected as the area grows larger. An example has been done for you. In each box, also make a simple drawing of the challenge you have identified.

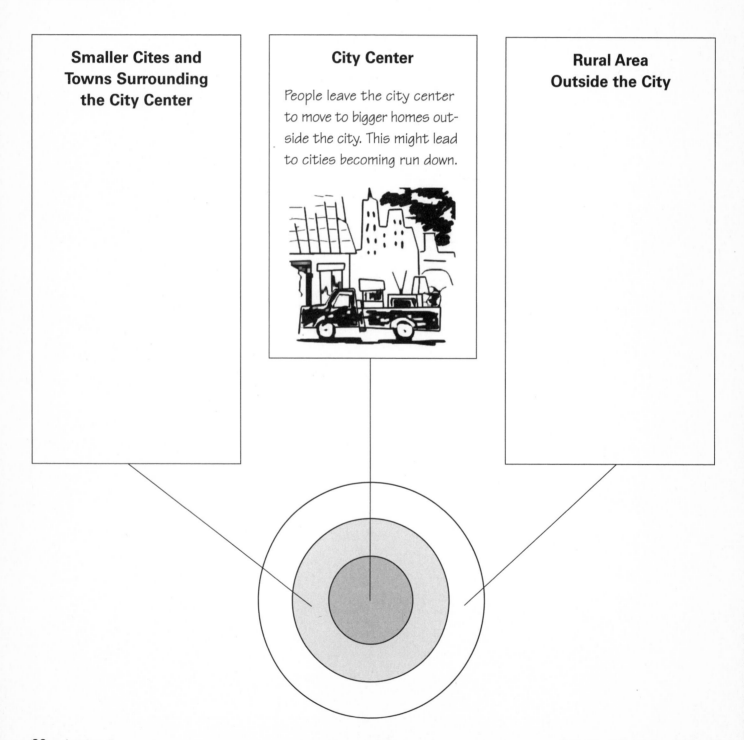

Smaller Cites and Towns Surrounding the City Center

City Center

People leave the city center to move to bigger homes outside the city. This might lead to cities becoming run down.

Rural Area Outside the City

© Teachers' Curriculum Institute

Read Sections 5.1 and 5.2. Then create an illustrated dictionary of the Geoterms by completing these tasks:

- Create a symbol or an illustration to represent each term.
- Write a definition of each term in your own words.
- Write a sentence that includes the term and the word *city*.

Geoterm and Symbol	Definition	Sentence
metropolitan area		
rural fringe		
suburb		
urban core		
urban fringe		
urban sprawl		

Urban Sprawl in North America: Where Will It End?

5.4 Portland, Oregon, 1973

After reading Section 5.4, identify three challenges facing Portland in 1973. Record them in the boxes below. Draw a line from each box to the part of the city most affected by that problem.

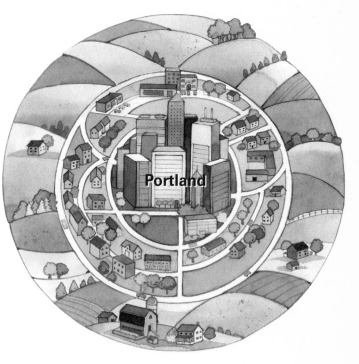

My interest group believes that this policy would be best for Portland:

We believe this is the best policy for these three reasons:

1.

2.

3.

5.5 Portland Plans for Smart Growth

Read Section 5.5 to find out what Portland did. Then complete the information below.

Portland chose to:

The results of this policy were:

1.

2.

3.

5.6 Toronto, Ontario, 1999

After reading Section 5.6, identify three challenges facing Toronto in 1999. Record them in the boxes below. Draw a line from each box to the part of the city most affected by that problem.

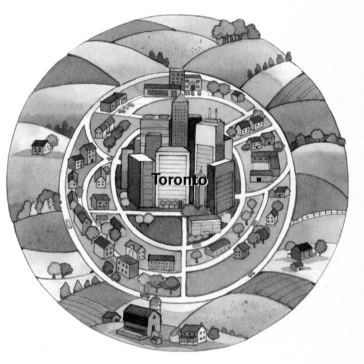

My interest group believes that this policy would be best for Toronto:

We believe this is the best policy for these three reasons:

1.

2.

3.

5.7 Toronto Plans for 30 Years of Growth

Read Section 5.7 to find out what Toronto did. Then complete the
information below.

Toronto chose to:

The results of this policy were:

1.

2.

3.

5.8 Atlanta, Georgia, 1998

After reading Section 5.8, identify three challenges facing Atlanta in 1998. Record them in the boxes below. Draw a line from each box to the part of the city most affected by that problem.

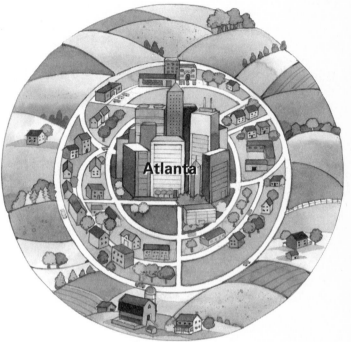

My interest group believes that this policy would be best for Atlanta:

We believe this is the best policy for these three reasons:

1.

2.

3.

5.9 Atlanta Fights Pollution with Public Transit

Read Section 5.9 to find out what Atlanta did. Then complete the information below.

Atlanta chose to:

The results of this policy were:

1.

2.

3.

Is urban sprawl happening in your area? If so, how is it affecting your life? Using what you have learned about urban planning, you will create a diagram of the area where you live. You will also make two recommendations about what could be done about urban sprawl in your area.

1. Decide which city closest to you is the urban core. Put its name in the center of the diagram.

2. Label the towns and cities that surround this city and make up the urban fringe.

3. Around the urban fringe, label the towns and cities that make up the rural fringe.

4. Around the drawing, list three problems of urban sprawl in your area. Each problem should relate to the urban core, the urban fringe, or the rural fringe. Draw a line from each problem to the appropriate area.

5. Write two recommendations about what could be done about urban sprawl in your area.

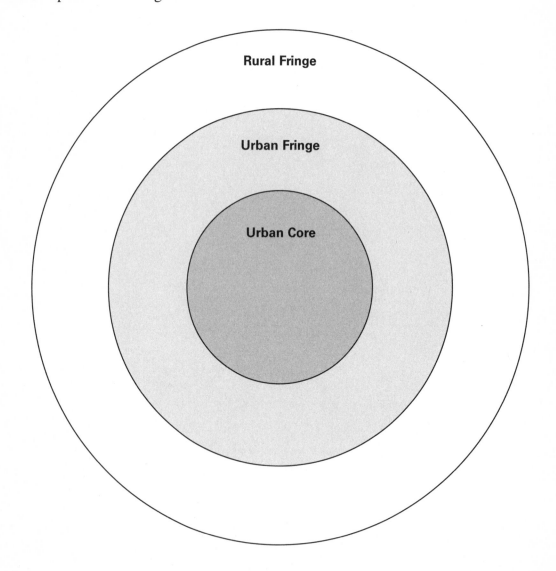

Below is part of a topographic map of Grand Canyon National Park. Locate Point A on the map. Then, with your finger, follow the line from Point A to Point B. You will be completing the elevation profile of a trip along this line. The elevation profile will be a cross-section of the topographic map. It will show how the elevation increases and decreases over the course of two miles.

Finish the elevation profile. The first half mile has been done for you.

Topography of Grand Canyon National Park (detail)

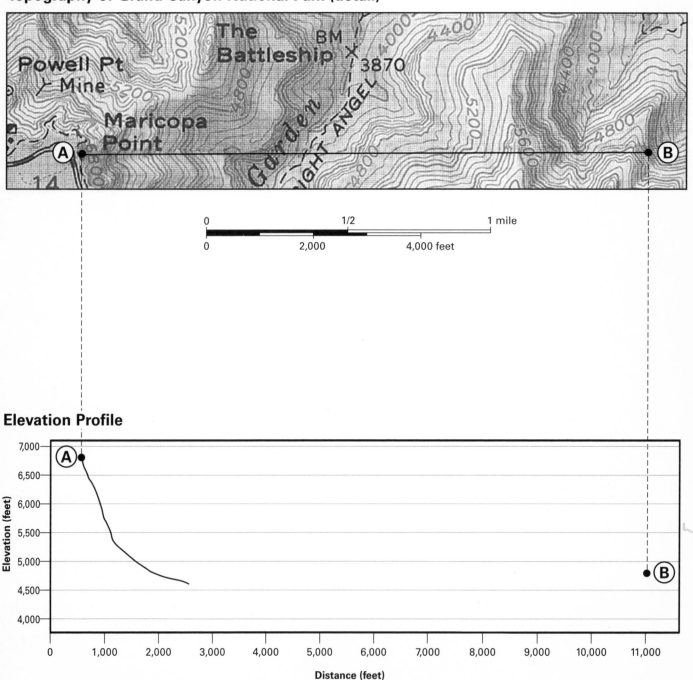

Elevation Profile

© Teachers' Curriculum Institute

Read Sections 6.1 and 6.2. Then create an illustrated dictionary of the Geoterms by completing these tasks:

- Create a symbol or an illustration to represent each term.
- Write a definition of each term in your own words.
- Write a sentence that includes the term and the words *national park*.

Geoterm and Symbol	Definition	Sentence
conservationist		
fauna		
flora		
topographic map		

READING NOTES 6

Read Sections 6.3 to 6.5. After reading each section, you will create an adventure tour for that park. A tour plan for the Grand Canyon is shown here as an example. It includes a map showing the route the tour will take. Follow these steps to create an adventure tour for each park you read about:

1. Turn to the section of Reading Notes 6 for that park.

2. On the topographic map of that park, draw the route your tour will take. Your tour must

   • connect all four major stops. Stops are shown with stars.

   • be exciting for tourists.

   • use transportation in an adventurous but realistic way.

3. In the tour plan for that park, use the map and your book to describe

   • how many days you will stay at each location. The total trip can't take more than 10 days.

   • the elevation at each stop (where the red star is).

   • what tourists will do at each stop (any activities your company has planned for them).

   • what tourists will see at each stop (flora, fauna, human features, physical features).

   • how tourists will get to the next stop (what mode of transportation they will use). See Step 4.

Tour Plan for Grand Canyon National Park

Stop 1: ___1___ day(s)
Hopi Point

Elevation: 6,500 feet

What you'll do:
• Rappel down Hopi Wall using rock-climbing equipment
• Visit Lookout Tower
• Drive along the South Rim in a four-wheel-drive vehicle

What you'll see:
• spectacular views of the canyon walls
• the dramatic cliffs of the Inferno
• Hopi Wall and Salt Creek

How you'll get to Stop 2: four-wheel-drive vehicle

Stop 2: ___2___ day(s)
El Tovar Hotel

Elevation: 6,900 feet

What you'll do:
• Have dinner and spend the night at the El Tovar Hotel
• Take a horseback tour down Bright Angel Trail along Garden Creek
• Hike Plateau Point and then continue on horseback to the Suspension Bridge on the Colorado River

What you'll see:
• Bright Angel Trail winding down 2,000-foot cliffs
• Garden Creek at the bottom of the canyon
• buildings and shops surrounding the South Rim

How you'll get to Stop 3: horseback

Stop 3: ___2___ day(s)
Granite Gorge

Elevation: 2,000 feet

What you'll do:
• White-water rafting on the Colorado River through Granite Gorge

What you'll see:
• suspension bridges spanning the river
• rapids along the River Trail and through Granite Gorge

How you'll get to Stop 4: raft

Stop 4: ___1___ day(s)
Yavapai Point

Elevation: 6,520 feet

What you'll do:
• Raft through the rapids
• Take a helicopter tour over the Colorado River, the Natural Arch, O'Neill Butte, Yaki Point, and Mather Point
• Land at Yavapai Point and visit the museum there

What you'll see:
• stunning aerial views of the canyon
• exhibits on geology and theories on how the Grand Canyon was formed at the Yavapai Point Museum

---

4. Decide what kind of transportation tourists will use to get from place
   to place and for the activities at each stop. Choose from list below.
   For each adventure tour, you cannot use any mode of transportation
   more than once.

helicopter

hiking gear

jet skis

rock-climbing equipment

kayaks

snowshoes

rafting gear

hang-gliding equipment

bicycles

horses

four-wheel-drive vehicles

cross-country skis

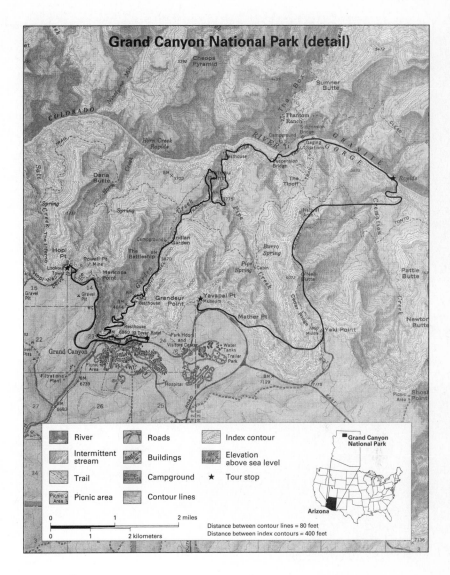

Grand Canyon National Park (detail)

River		Roads		Index contour
Intermittent stream		Buildings		Elevation above sea level
Trail		Campground	★	Tour stop
Picnic area		Contour lines		

0   1   2 miles
0   1   2 kilometers

Distance between contour lines = 80 feet
Distance between index contours = 400 feet

Grand Canyon National Park

Arizona

6.3 Waterton-Glacier International Peace Park

Follow the directions on pages 48 and 49 to complete the tour plan and
map for this park.

Tour Plan for Waterton-Glacier International Peace Park

Stop 1: _____ day(s)
Lake McDonald

Elevation:

What you'll do:

What you'll see:

How you'll get to Stop 2:

Stop 2: _____ day(s)
_____

Elevation:

What you'll do:

What you'll see:

How you'll get to Stop 3:

Stop 3: _____ day(s)
_____

Elevation:

What you'll do:

What you'll see:

How you'll get to Stop 4:

Stop 4: _____ day(s)
_____

Elevation:

What you'll do:

What you'll see:

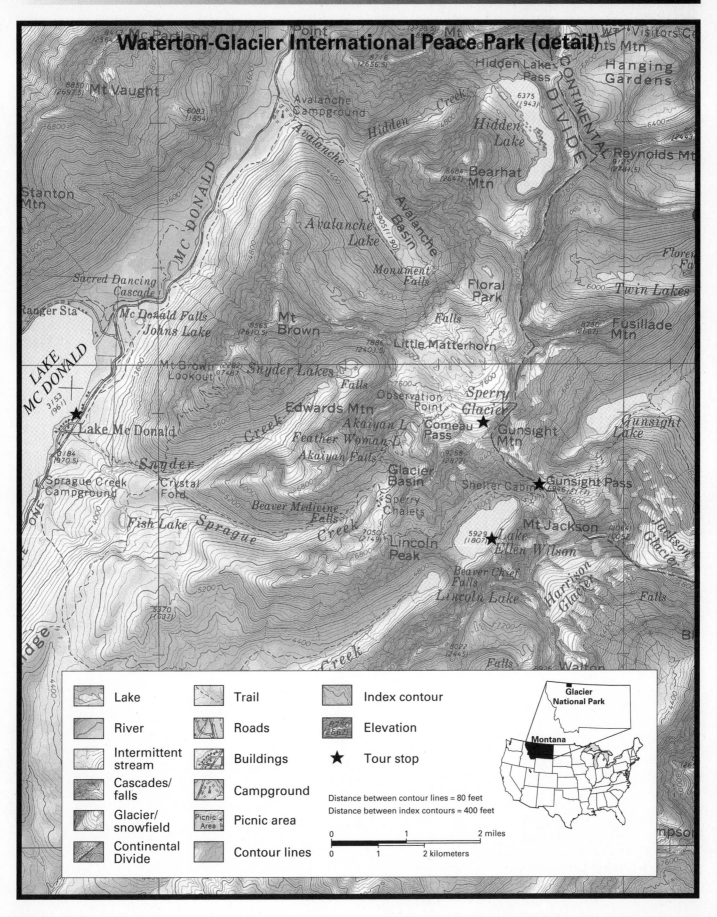

Waterton-Glacier International Peace Park (detail)

Legend:

Lake	
River	
Intermittent stream	
Cascades/falls	
Glacier/snowfield	
Continental Divide	
Trail	
Roads	
Buildings	
Campground	
Picnic area	
Contour lines	
Index contour	
Elevation	
★ Tour stop	

Distance between contour lines = 80 feet
Distance between index contours = 400 feet

0   1   2 miles
0 1   2 kilometers

Glacier National Park
Montana

6.4 Prince Edward Island National Park
Follow the directions on pages 48 and 49 to complete the tour plan and
map for this park.

Tour Plan for Prince Edward Island National Park

Stop 1: _____ day(s)
Green Gables house

Elevation:

What you'll do:

What you'll see:

How you'll get to Stop 2:

Stop 2: _____ day(s)
_____

Elevation:

What you'll do:

What you'll see:

How you'll get to Stop 3:

Stop 3: _____ day(s)
_____

Elevation:

What you'll do:

What you'll see:

How you'll get to Stop 4:

Stop 4: _____ day(s)
_____

Elevation:

What you'll do:

What you'll see:

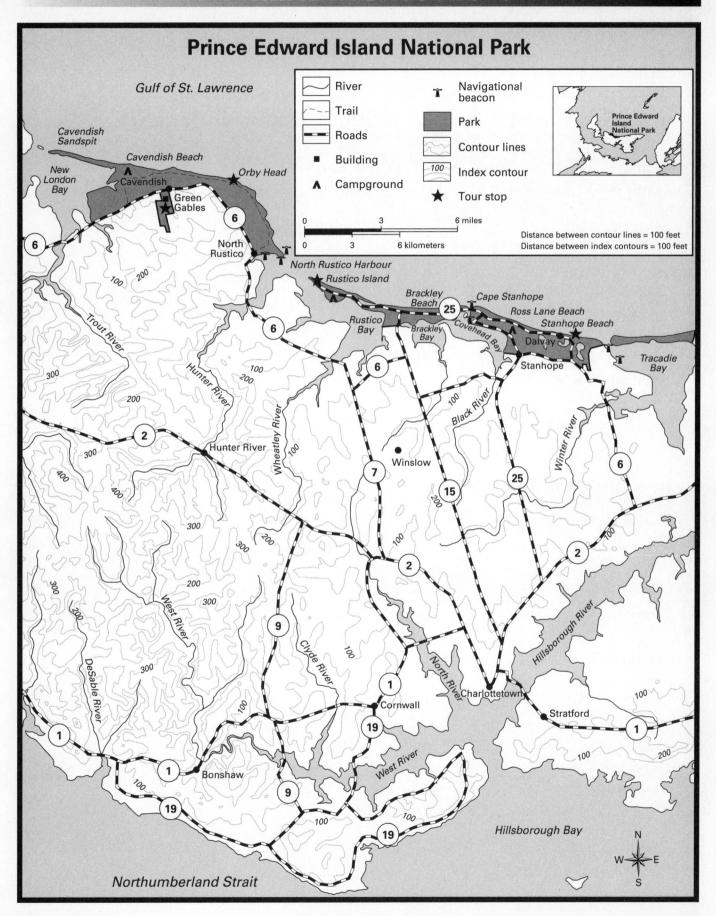

Prince Edward Island National Park

Gulf of St. Lawrence

Legend:
- River
- Trail
- Roads
- Building
- Campground
- Navigational beacon
- Park
- Contour lines
- 100 Index contour
- Tour stop

0 3 6 miles
0 3 6 kilometers

Distance between contour lines = 100 feet
Distance between index contours = 100 feet

Prince Edward Island National Park

Cavendish Sandspit
Cavendish Beach
New London Bay
Cavendish
Orby Head
Green Gables
North Rustico
North Rustico Harbour
Rustico Island
Brackley Beach
Cape Stanhope
Ross Lane Beach
Stanhope Beach
Rustico Bay
Brackley Bay
Covehead Bay
Dalvay
Stanhope
Tracadie Bay
Trout River
Hunter River
Wheatley River
Black River
Winter River
Hunter River
Winslow
Clyde River
West River
DeSable River
Cornwall
North River
Charlottetown
Stratford
Hillsborough River
Bonshaw
West River
Hillsborough Bay
Northumberland Strait

N
W E
S

6.5 Yosemite National Park
Follow the directions on pages 48 and 49 to complete the tour plan and
map for this park.

Tour Plan for Yosemite National Park

Stop 1: _____ day(s)
Lower Yosemite Fall

Elevation:

What you'll do:

What you'll see:

How you'll get to Stop 2:

Stop 2: _____ day(s)
_____

Elevation:

What you'll do:

What you'll see:

How you'll get to Stop 3:

Stop 3: _____ day(s)
_____

Elevation:

What you'll do:

What you'll see:

How you'll get to Stop 4:

Stop 4: _____ day(s)
_____

Elevation:

What you'll do:

What you'll see:

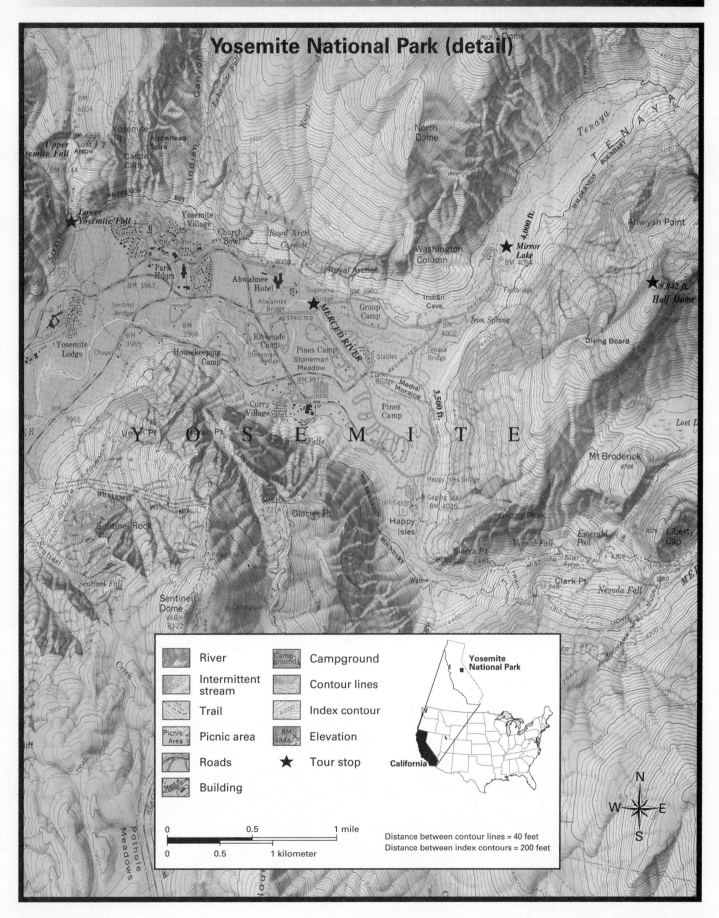

Yosemite National Park (detail)

Upper Yosemite Fall
Lost Arrow
Yosemite Pt
Arrowhead Spire
Castle Cliffs
BM 6604
BM 6936
BM 5144
Lower Yosemite Fall
Yosemite Village
Church Bowl
Visitor Center
Royal Arch Cascade
Royal Arches
North Dome
Washington Column
Mirror Lake
BM 4094
Ahwiyah Point
8,842 ft. Half Dome
Park Hdqrs
BM 3967
Ahwahnee Hotel
Ahwahnee Bridge
Sugarpine Bridge
BM 3980
Indian Cave
Iron Spring
Diving Board
Sentinel Bridge
BM 3966
Riverside Camp
Stoneman Bridge
Group Camp
BM 4002
Stables
Tenaya Bridge
Yosemite Lodge
Chapel
BM 3965
Housekeeping Camp
Pines Camp
Stoneman Meadow
BM 3972
Clarks Bridge
Medial Moraine
Curry Village
Pines Camp
BM 3965
YOSEMITE
Staircase Falls
Happy Isles Bridge
Gaging Sta
BM 4035
Mt Broderick
6706
Lost L
Sentinel Rock
WILDERNESS
BM 7214
Glacier Pt
Trail Center
Happy Isles
Sierra Pt
Grizzly Peak
Vernal Fall
Emerald Pool
Liberty Cap
Sentinel Dome
VABM 8122
Campground
Clark Pt
Nevada Fall
Pothole Meadows
Creek

Legend

	River
	Intermittent stream
	Trail
Picnic Area	Picnic area
	Roads
	Building
Campground	Campground
	Contour lines
4,000	Index contour
BM 4844	Elevation
★	Tour stop

Yosemite National Park
California

0   0.5   1 mile
0   0.5   1 kilometer

Distance between contour lines = 40 feet
Distance between index contours = 200 feet

Create a poster to let people know about the dangers to national parks in North America. Use your Reading Notes and additional research to help you. Your poster can be about any endangered national park in the United States or Canada. Plan your poster here. It should contain these things:

- an attention-grabbing title
- the name of the park
- three reasons the park is in danger
- an illustration of one way the park is in danger
- two things people can do to help protect the park

Make your poster on a large sheet of paper. At the bottom of your poster, list at least three sources you used to gather information, like encyclopedias or Web sites.

Read Sections 7.1 and 7.2. Then create an illustrated dictionary of the Geoterms by completing these tasks:

- Create a symbol or an illustration to represent each term.
- Write a definition of each term in your own words.
- Write a sentence that includes the term.

Geoterm and Symbol	Definition	Sentence
consumption		
developed country		
developing country		
gross domestic product (GDP)		
per capita		

Analyze the food consumption cartogram with your class. Then, with your group, read Section 7.3 and answer the questions below.

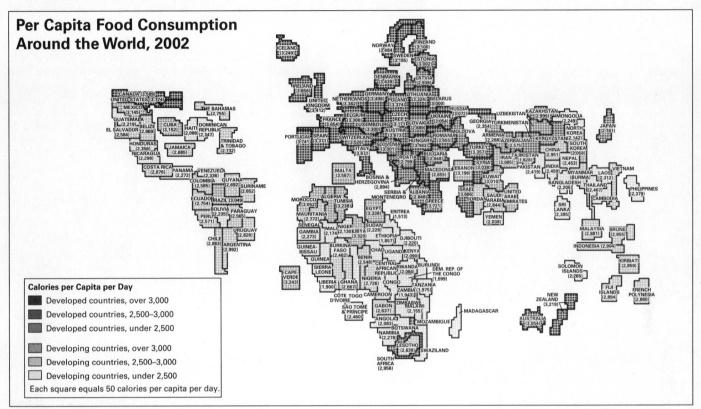

Per Capita Food Consumption Around the World, 2002

Calories per Capita per Day
- Developed countries, over 3,000
- Developed countries, 2,500–3,000
- Developed countries, under 2,500
- Developing countries, over 3,000
- Developing countries, 2,500–3,000
- Developing countries, under 2,500

Each square equals 50 calories per capita per day.

Sources: *Food and Agriculture Organization of the United Nations,* "Food Balance Sheet 2002," faostat.fao.org/faostat/. *Population Reference Bureau,* www.prb.org.

7.3 Food Consumption Patterns

How many calories per day does the average person need to live a healthy life?

List three countries that consume a high amount of calories per capita, per day. What type of country tends to consume more calories per capita? Why do you think that is?

List three countries that consume a low amount of calories per capita, per day. What type of country tends to consume fewer calories per capita? Why do you think that is?

Analyze the oil consumption cartogram with your class. Then, with your group, read Section 7.4 and answer the questions below.

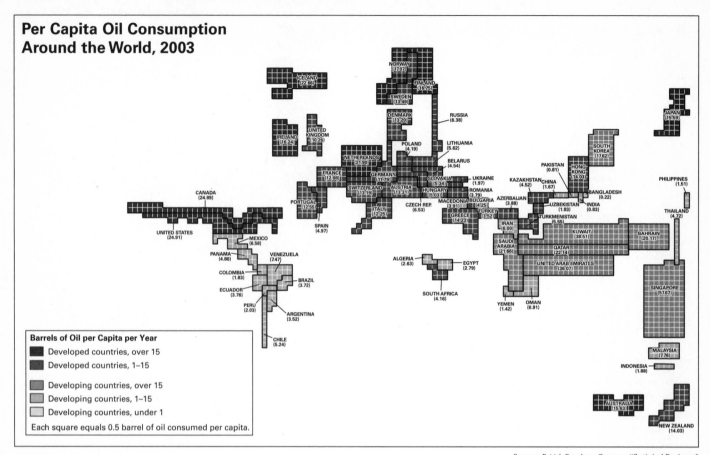

Per Capita Oil Consumption Around the World, 2003

Barrels of Oil per Capita per Year
- Developed countries, over 15
- Developed countries, 1–15
- Developing countries, over 15
- Developing countries, 1–15
- Developing countries, under 1

Each square equals 0.5 barrel of oil consumed per capita.

Sources: *British Petroleum Company*, "Statistical Review of World Energy," www.bp.com. *Population Reference Bureau*, "2004 World Population Data Sheet," www.prb.org. *World Bank, World Development Indicators 2003*, Washington, D.C.: World Bank, 2003.

7.4 Oil Consumption Patterns

What is oil used for?

Which developed countries consume the most oil per capita? Why do you think that is?

Which developing countries consume the most oil per capita? Why do you think that is?

Analyze the computer consumption cartogram with your class. Then, with your group, read Section 7.5 and answer the questions below.

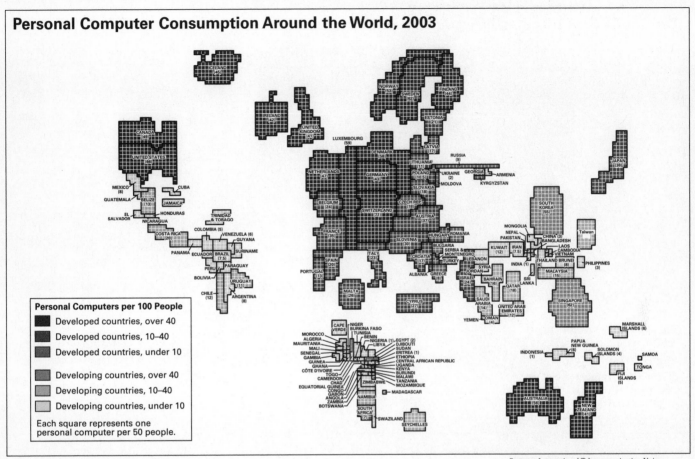

Personal Computer Consumption Around the World, 2003

Personal Computers per 100 People

- ■ Developed countries, over 40
- ▨ Developed countries, 10–40
- ▨ Developed countries, under 10

- ▨ Developing countries, over 40
- ▨ Developing countries, 10–40
- ▨ Developing countries, under 10

Each square represents one personal computer per 50 people.

Sources: *International Telecommunication Union,* "Internet Indicators: Hosts, Users, and Number of PCs," www.itu.int/. *Population Reference Bureau,* www.prb.org.

7.5 Computer and Internet Use Patterns

What are computers and the Internet used for?

Which countries have the most access to technology? Why do you think that is?

Which countries have the least access to technology? Why do you think that is?

Analyze the gross domestic product (GDP) cartogram with your class.
Then, with your group, read Section 7.6 and answer the questions below.

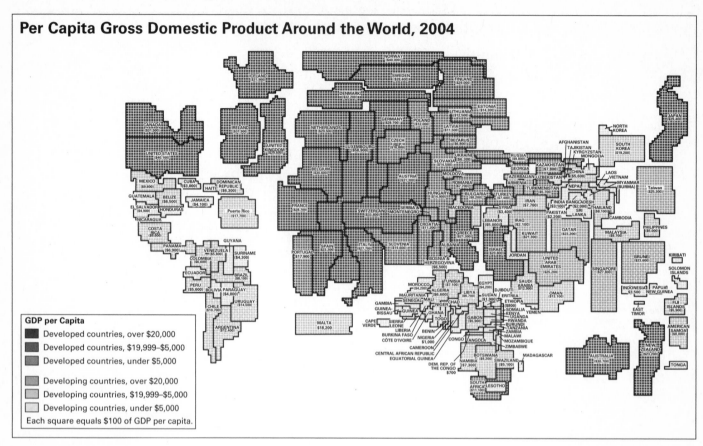

Per Capita Gross Domestic Product Around the World, 2004

GDP per Capita

■ Developed countries, over $20,000
■ Developed countries, $19,999–$5,000
■ Developed countries, under $5,000

▨ Developing countries, over $20,000
▨ Developing countries, $19,999–$5,000
▢ Developing countries, under $5,000
Each square equals $100 of GDP per capita.

Sources: *Central Intelligence Agency*, "The World Factbook,"
www.cia.gov. *Population Reference Bureau*, www.prb.org.

7.6 The World's Greatest Producers

What three important factors contribute to the United States' high GDP?

How does education affect GDP in the United States?

How does the American work ethic affect GDP?

How do you think a country's GDP affects its citizens' ability to consume?

Suppose the consumer class continues to grow and consume like the United States and other developed countries. What might happen to the world? Create a simple political cartoon to show your ideas.

In your cartoon, show at least two changes that might happen. These could be environmental, health, quality-of-life, or economic changes. Your cartoon should also have these things:

- exaggerated details
- symbols that represent, or stand for, something else
- labels that identify parts of the cartoon
- a caption

Think of someone you know who has moved. Draw an arrow that shows where he or she moved from and to. Write the person's name on the arrow. Do this for as many people as you can think of.

Share your map with a partner. Tell him or her the reasons one of the people on your map moved.

Migration to the United States: The Impact on People and Places **65**

GEOTERMS 8

Read Sections 8.1 and 8.2. Then create an illustrated dictionary of the
Geoterms by completing these tasks:

- Create a symbol or an illustration to represent each term.
- Write a definition of each term in your own words.
- Write a sentence that includes the term and the word *person* or *people*.

Geoterm and Symbol	Definition	Sentence
emigrate		
immigrate		
migration stream		
pull factor		
push factor		
refugee		

Follow these steps to complete your Reading Notes:

1. Read Sections 8.3 and 8.4. List examples of each push and pull factor you read about.

2. During the interviews, add any new examples of push and pull factors you learn about to your notes. You might also learn about how immigration affects the United States and the countries left behind. List those examples in your notes for Sections 8.5 and 8.6.

3. After the interviews, read Sections 8.5 and 8.6. Add any new examples you read about to your notes.

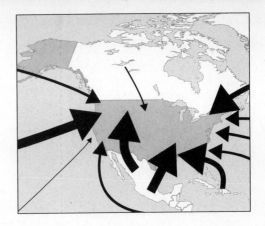

8.3 What Push Factors Drive Emigration?

Examples of political push factors:

Examples of environmental push factors:

Examples of economic push factors:

8.4 What Pull Factors Draw Immigration?

Examples of quality-of-life pull factors:

Examples of family pull factors:

Examples of education pull factors:

8.5 How Does Immigration Affect the U.S.?

Examples of economic impacts (jobs):

Examples of economic impacts (taxes):

Examples of cultural impacts (neighborhoods, foods, and holidays):

8.6 How Does Emigration Affect the Homelands People Leave Behind?

Examples of economic impacts (brain drain and gain):

Examples of social impacts (divided families, community improvements):

Examples of political impacts (working for better government):

Interview someone who immigrated to the United States. Ask the four questions below, and record the person's answers. Based on what you learn from the interview, you may want to ask more questions. Record your questions and their answers.

Interview Notes

Person's name: _____ Age: _____

Country of birth: _____

Current residence (U.S. state): _____

Question 1: What pushed you to leave your country?

Answer:

Question 2: What pulled you to America?

Answer:

Question 3: How has your immigration affected your life and your new community in America?

Answer:

Question 4: How has your emigration affected your home country?

Answer:

Additional questions and answers:

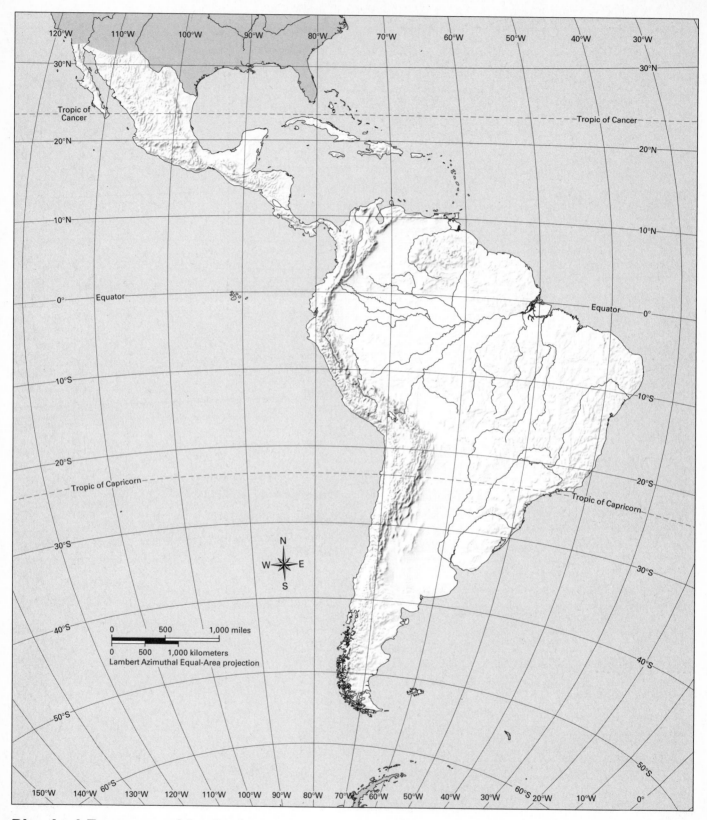

Physical Features of Latin America

© Teachers' Curriculum Institute

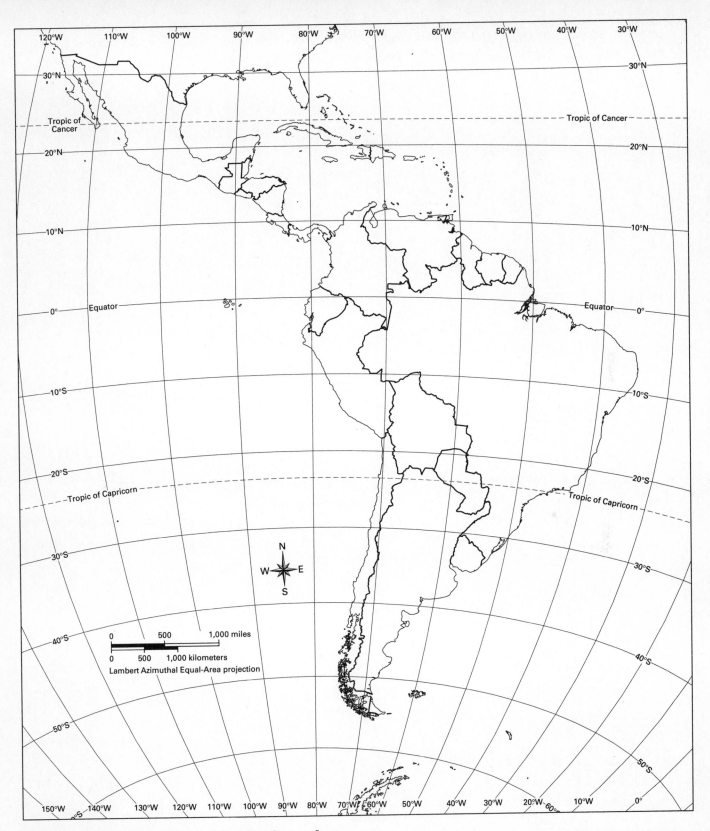

30°N
Tropic of Cancer
20°N
10°N
Equator 0°
10°S
Tropic of Capricorn
20°S
30°S
40°S
50°S

120°W 110°W 100°W 90°W 80°W 70°W 60°W 50°W 40°W 30°W

150°W 140°W 130°W 120°W 110°W 100°W 90°W 80°W 70°W 60°W 50°W 40°W 30°W 20°W 10°W 0°

N
W E
S

0   500   1,000 miles
0   500   1,000 kilometers
Lambert Azimuthal Equal-Area projection

Political Boundaries of Latin America

Think about a city you know or recently visited. In the space below, draw and label some of its main features. You might include important buildings, main streets, major landmarks, neighborhoods, and homes. Then complete the chart.

What are the best characteristics of this city?	**What are the worst characteristics of this city?**

Read Sections 9.1 and 9.2. Then create an illustrated dictionary of the Geoterms by completing these tasks:

- Create a symbol or an illustration to represent each term.
- Write a definition of each term in your own words.
- Write a sentence that includes the term and the words *Mexico City*.

Geoterm and Symbol	Definition	Sentence
rural decline		
spatial inequality		
standard of living		
urbanization		

Neighborhood Visit 1

Part 1: Read Section 9.3. Then answer these questions:

What challenges do farmers face in Mexico's countryside?

Why do many farmers decide to migrate to the city?

Part 2: Listen carefully to the interview. Then complete as much of the survey as you can.

Neighborhood Survey	
Population density	
Green space per person	
Percentage of homes built with good materials	
Percentage of people over age 15 with education beyond primary school	
Percentage of homes with water	
Number of police officers	

Part 3: Color the area on the map where you think this neighborhood is located. Then complete the sentence. Include three details that support your answer. Use your Reading Notes, your survey, or the maps on Student Handout 9 to help you.

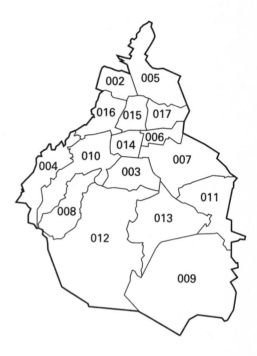

I think we visited a neighborhood in

because...

Neighborhood Visit 2

Part 1: Read Section 9.4. Then answer these questions: In what ways is Mexico City still growing?

What problems is Mexico City experiencing as a result of its rapid growth?

Part 2: Listen carefully to the interview. Then complete as much of the survey as you can.

Neighborhood Survey	
Population density	
Green space per person	
Percentage of homes built with good materials	
Percentage of people over age 15 with education beyond primary school	
Percentage of homes with water	
Number of police officers	

Part 3: Color the area on the map where you think this neighborhood is located. Then complete the sentence. Include three details that support your answer. Use your Reading Notes, your survey, or the maps on Student Handout 9 to help you.

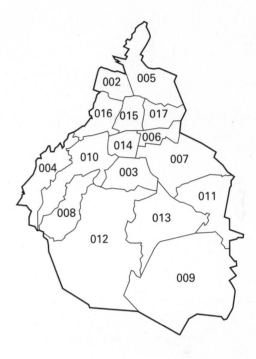

I think we visited a neighborhood in

because…

Neighborhood Visit 3

Part 1: Read the introduction to Section 9.5 and the subsection "The 'Have Nots' Struggle to Survive." Then answer these questions:

What are the living conditions for Mexico City's recent migrants?

What are the living conditions for Mexico City's working poor?

Part 2: Listen carefully to the interview. Then complete as much of the survey as you can.

Neighborhood Survey	
Population density	
Green space per person	
Percentage of homes built with good materials	
Percentage of people over age 15 with education beyond primary school	
Percentage of homes with water	
Number of police officers	

Part 3: Color the area on the map where you think this neighborhood is located. Then complete the sentence. Include three details that support your answer. Use your Reading Notes, your survey, or the maps on Student Handout 9 to help you.

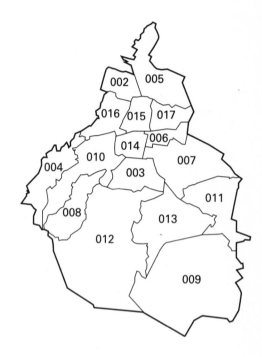

I think we visited a neighborhood in

because…

Neighborhood Visit 4

Part 1: Read the subsection of Section 9.5 called "The 'Haves' Live Well." Then answer these questions:

What types of jobs do the middle class of Mexico City have? How does this affect their lifestyle?

Who belongs to Mexico City's upper class? What type of lifestyle do they have?

Part 2: Listen carefully to the interview. Then complete as much of the survey as you can.

Neighborhood Survey	
Population density	
Green space per person	
Percentage of homes built with good materials	
Percentage of people over age 15 with education beyond primary school	
Percentage of homes with water	
Number of police officers	

Part 3: Color the area on the map where you think this neighborhood is located. Then complete the sentence. Include three details that support your answer. Use your Reading Notes, your survey, or the maps on Student Handout 9 to help you.

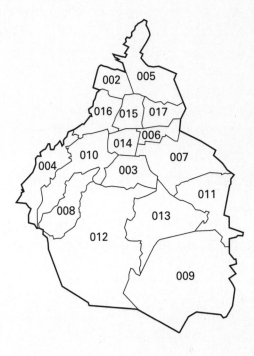

I think we visited a neighborhood in

because…

Look carefully at the photograph your teacher is projecting. Talk about the questions below with your partner, and record your answers.

1. Find four interesting or important details in the photograph. Quickly sketch them below.

2. This family is preserving its traditional culture. What do you see in the photograph that shows this?

3. This family has also adapted to modern life. What do you see in the photograph that shows this?

4. Do you think this family is more traditional or more modern? Support your answer with at least three details from the photograph.

Read Sections 10.1 and 10.2. Then create an illustrated dictionary of
the Geoterms by completing these tasks:

- Create a symbol or an illustration to represent each term.
- Write a definition of each term in your own words.
- Write a sentence that includes the term and the phrase *highland Maya*.

Geoterm and Symbol	Definition	Sentence
adaptation		
indigenous peoples		
subsistence farming		
traditional culture		

Follow these steps to complete the Reading Notes for Sections 10.3 to 10.7:

1. Read the section about the topic you have been assigned. Complete the notes for that section.

2. Before each presentation, read and complete the notes for that section.

3. After each presentation, add any new details to your notes.

10.3 A Strong Sense of Community

In what ways have the highland Maya preserved their traditional culture?

In what ways have the highland Maya adapted to modern life?

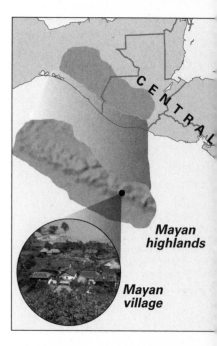

Mayan highlands

Mayan village

10.4 The Traditional Home and Family

In what ways have the highland Maya preserved their traditional culture?

In what ways have the highland Maya adapted to modern life?

10.5 Changing Ways of Work

In what ways have the highland Maya preserved their traditional culture?

In what ways have the highland Maya adapted to modern life?

0   150   300 miles

0   150   300 kilometers

Albers Conic Equal-Area projection

10.6 Making the Most of Market Day

In what ways have the highland Maya preserved their traditional culture?

In what ways have the highland Maya adapted to modern life?

10.7 Keeping Mayan Traditions Alive

In what ways have the highland Maya preserved their traditional culture?

In what ways have the highland Maya adapted to modern life?

Complete this illustration to show what you have learned about the Maya in the highlands of Guatemala and southern Mexico.

- Color or draw details that show how this Mayan family is preserving its traditional culture. Color or draw at least four details.

- Color or draw details that show how this family is adapting to modern life. Color or draw at least four details.

- Include at least one detail from each aspect of highland Maya life you studied: "community," "home and family," "work," "market day," and "traditions."

- Label each detail you color or draw. Write a short explanation of how each item represents ways this family is preserving its traditional culture or adapting to modern life. An example is given for you.

Traditional Mayan homes have simple wooden chairs like these.

Draw an outline map of the Caribbean below.

- Label any physical features and countries you know.
- Use symbols and colors to show things you know about the Caribbean.
- Create a legend that identifies your symbols and colors.
- Title your map, and add a compass rose.

Read Sections 11.1 and 11.2. Then create an illustrated dictionary of the
Geoterms by completing these tasks:

• Create a symbol or an illustration to represent each term.

• Write a definition of each term in your own words.

• Write a sentence that includes the term.

Geoterm and Symbol	Definition	Sentence
El Niño		
extreme weather		
meteorology		
natural disaster		
tropical cyclone		

As you read each of Sections 11.4 to 11.8, complete the Reading Notes for that section.

11.8 Cleaning Up After a Natural Disaster

Write a summary of what happens after a hurricane. Include these terms in your summary: *rebuilding, relief agencies, cleaning up, Caribbean*.

11.7 Landfall: A Natural Disaster Begins

Write a summary of what happens when a hurricane makes landfall. Include these terms in your summary: *wind, rain, storm surge, Caribbean*.

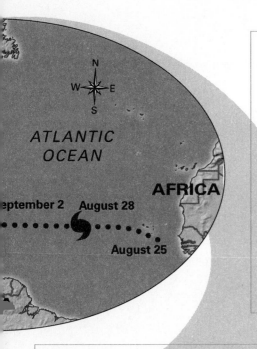

11.4 Extreme Weather: A Hurricane Is Born

Write a summary of how a hurricane is formed. Include these terms in your summary: *Africa, Atlantic Ocean, warm and moist air, thunderstorms, tropical disturbance, Coriolis effect, tropical cyclone.*

11.5 Inside a Monster Storm

Draw a simple diagram of the inside of a hurricane. Include and label these parts: *eye, eye wall, rainbands.*

11.6 Tracking and Preparing for a Hurricane

Write a summary of how people track and prepare for a hurricane. Include these terms in your summary: *meteorologist, hurricane watch, hurricane warning, Saffir-Simpson scale.*

Create a pamphlet for Jamaica's Office of Disaster Preparedness and Emergency Management. The pamphlet will help teach people about hurricanes. Plan your pamphlet here.

Fold a sheet of paper in half to make your pamphlet. Your pamphlet should have

- a front cover with a catchy title and a colorful visual.
- a section on what causes hurricanes and how they gain strength. Include a title and an illustration.
- a section on how people can prepare for hurricanes. Include a title, at least five tips or important pieces of information, and a helpful illustration.
- a back cover with interesting facts about hurricanes in the Caribbean. You might include details about past storms, such as the amount of destruction caused by hurricanes.
- creative touches to make your pamphlet stand out.
- writing that uses correct grammar and spelling.

Imagine that your community has recently been given several square miles of new land. This new land contains a small forest, a creek that empties into a small lake, and flat, grassy meadows. What should your community do with this new land?

Choose one of the options below. At the bottom of the page, sketch what you propose the area should look like. Be prepared to explain your proposal and why it is the best option.

A. Make the land into a public park. Include hiking and biking trails, a dock for small boats, a swimming area, picnic tables, and sports fields.

B. Develop the land. Build houses for low-income people in the community and a shopping area to provide jobs for people living in this area.

C. Leave the land as it is. Don't allow people to use the area.

D. Other idea (describe it).

Read Sections 12.1 and 12.2. Then create an illustrated dictionary of the Geoterms by completing these tasks:

- Create a symbol or an illustration to represent each term.
- Write a definition of each term in your own words.
- Write a sentence that includes the term and the word *rainforest*.

Geoterm and Symbol	Definition	Sentence
biodiversity		
carbon-oxygen cycle		
deforestation		
sustainable development		
tropical rainforest		

Read the section of Chapter 12 (Sections 12.3 to 12.8) that matches the rainforest group you have been assigned. Complete the Reading Notes for that group. Use the information from each news report to complete the notes for the other rainforest groups. Then complete the Reading Notes for Section 12.9.

12.3 What Native Amazonians Want

When did this group come to the rainforest? How do they use its resources?

We want...

What do they want? How do they defend their position?

12.4 What Rubber Tappers Want

When did this group come to the rainforest? How do they use its resources?

We want...

What do they want? How do they defend their position?

12.5 What Loggers Want

When did this group come to the rainforest? How do they use its resources?

We want...

What do they want? How do they defend their position?

12.6 What Settlers Want

When did this group come to the rainforest? How do they use its resources?

What do they want?
How do they defend
their position?

We want...

12.7 What Cattle Ranchers Want

When did this group come to the rainforest? How do they use its resources?

What do they want?
How do they defend
their position?

We want...

12.8 What Environmental Groups Want

When did this group come to the rainforest? How do they use its resources?

What do they want?
How do they defend
their position?

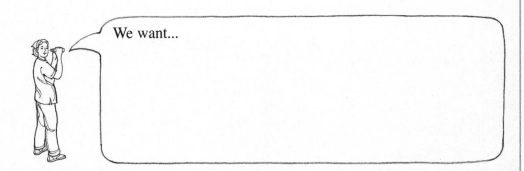

We want...

12.9 Ideas for Reducing Land Use Conflict

People have different ideas about how to address land use conflict in the rainforest. Which two ideas would you recommend?

1.

2.

Which rainforest groups' needs would be met by these two ideas?
Sketch and label each group below. In each speech bubble, have
that group explain how your ideas will meet their needs.

| Name of group | Name of group | Name of group | Name of group |

Write a letter to the Brazilian government. Explain your ideas about how to best preserve and use the resources of the Amazon rainforest. Your letter should follow this format:

- a proper greeting (for example, *Dear Ambassador* or *Dear Consul*)
- an introductory paragraph that identifies at least four groups who want to use or preserve the rainforest
- a paragraph that describes at least two actions that you think will best preserve and use the rainforest's resources
- a paragraph that explains how these actions will meet the needs or concerns of the groups you identified
- a proper closing (for instance, *Sincerely*)

1. In the space below, list or draw six things you typically do every day.
   You might include daily routines, such as riding the bus to school.
   Or you might include activities, like going to soccer practice.

2. Examine the transparency your teacher is projecting.
   - List or draw three details about the physical geography of
     this location.

   - How might your routines and activities change if you lived here?
     Why might they change?

   - How do you think the physical geography of this location influences
     the routines and activities of the people who live here?

Read Sections 13.1 and 13.2. Then create an illustrated dictionary of the Geoterms by completing these tasks:

- Create a symbol or an illustration to represent each term.
- Write a definition of each term in your own words.
- Write a sentence that includes the term and the words *mountainous region*.

Geoterm and Symbol	Definition	Sentence
altitudinal zonation		
snow line		
terracing		
tree line		
vertical trade		

Part 1: Physical Characteristics

Read the section of Chapter 13 that corresponds with your assigned elevation zone. Record the elevation range and at least two other physical characteristics of that zone. Illustrate *each* of those two items.

13.6 The Icy High Elevations: Tierra Helada

Elevation range: (_____ – _____) feet above sea level

Physical characteristics:

13.5 The Cool Highlands: Tierra Fría

Elevation range: (_____ – _____) feet above sea level

Physical characteristics:

13.4 The Pleasant Uplands: Tierra Templada

Elevation range: (_____ – _____) feet above sea level

Physical characteristics:

13.3 The Tropical Lowlands: Tierra Caliente

Elevation range: (_____ – _____) feet above sea level

Physical characteristics:

Part 2: Human Adaptations

Find the three graphics that show human adaptations in your assigned elevation zone. Write their letters below. Check your answers with your managing editor (teacher). Then write a short caption that explains how each graphic shows how people have adapted to living in this zone.

Graphic ___ Caption:

Graphic ___ Caption:

Graphic ___ Caption:

Graphic ___ Caption:

Graphic ___ Caption:

Graphic ___ Caption:

Graphic ___ Caption:

Graphic ___ Caption:

Graphic ___ Caption:

Graphic ___ Caption:

Graphic ___ Caption:

Graphic ___ Caption:

The World

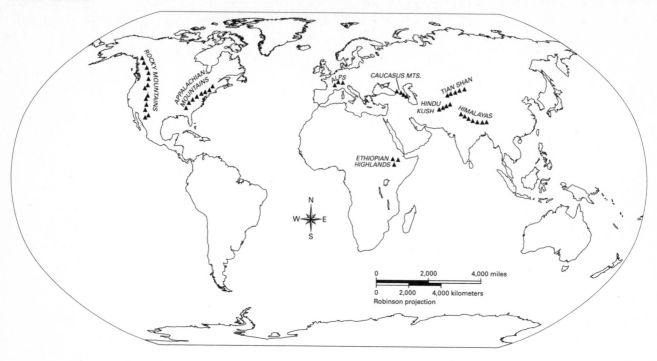

1. On the map, circle or highlight a mountainous region you would like to learn more about.

2. Read a newspaper, magazine, or Internet article about how people live in this region. Attach the article to this page.

3. Near this mountainous region on your map, draw and label symbols to represent at least two physical characteristics of the region.

4. Briefly describe the adaptations people have made to life in this region.

5. In what ways is life in this region similar to life in the central Andes? In what ways is it different? What might explain these similarities and differences?

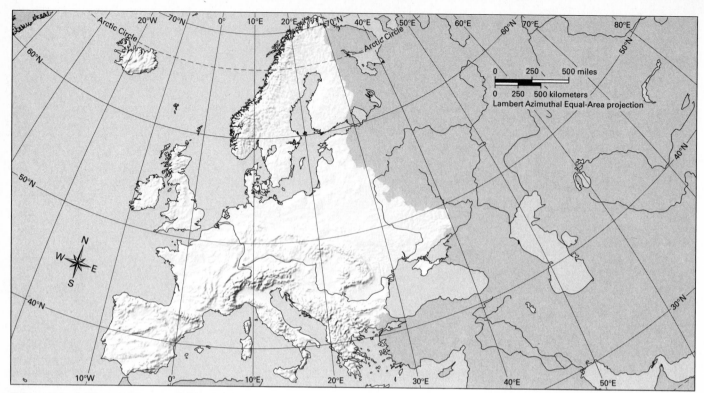

Physical Features of Europe

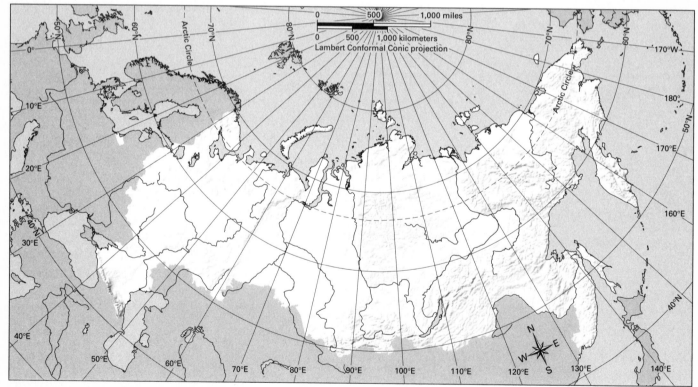

Physical Features of Russia

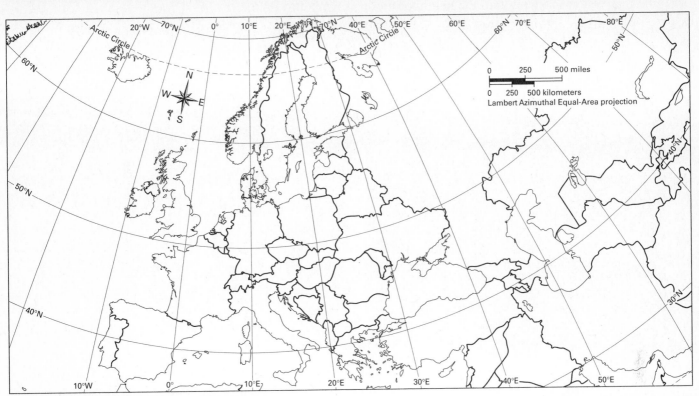

Political Boundaries of Europe

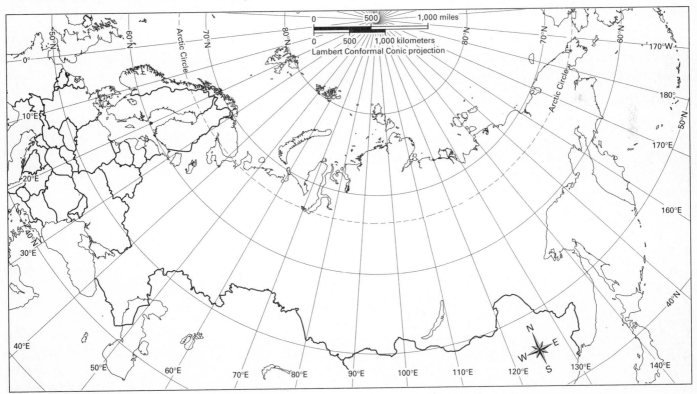

Political Boundaries of Russia

Imagine that you are moving into the neighborhood shown below. Which backyard would you choose? Why?

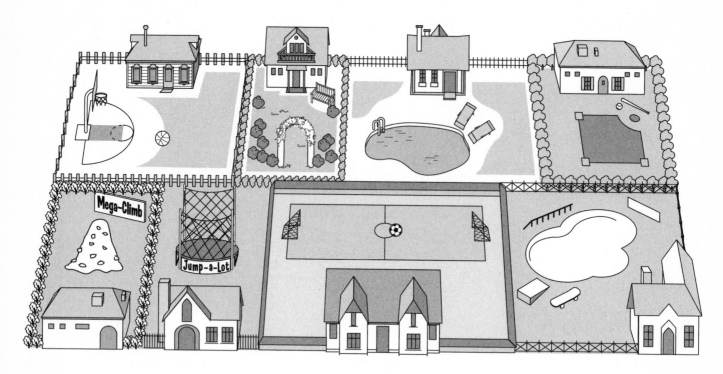

One of your new neighbors proposes that the fences should be taken down and a common backyard formed. List two advantages and two disadvantages of this plan. Then explain why you would support or disapprove of your neighbor's proposal.

Advantages:

Disadvantages:

I support/disapprove of this proposal because
     (circle one)

Read Sections 14.1 and 14.2. Then create an illustrated dictionary of the
Geoterms by completing these tasks:

- Create a symbol or an illustration to represent each term.
- Write a definition of each term in your own words.
- Write a sentence that includes the term and the words *European Union*.

Geoterm and Symbol	Definition	Sentence
centrifugal force		
centripetal force		
common market		
supranational cooperation		

Read each of Sections 14.3, 14.4, and 14.5. Answer the questions in the arrows for that section. Then compare what you read to what you experienced in class.

14.3 Economic Cooperation in the EU

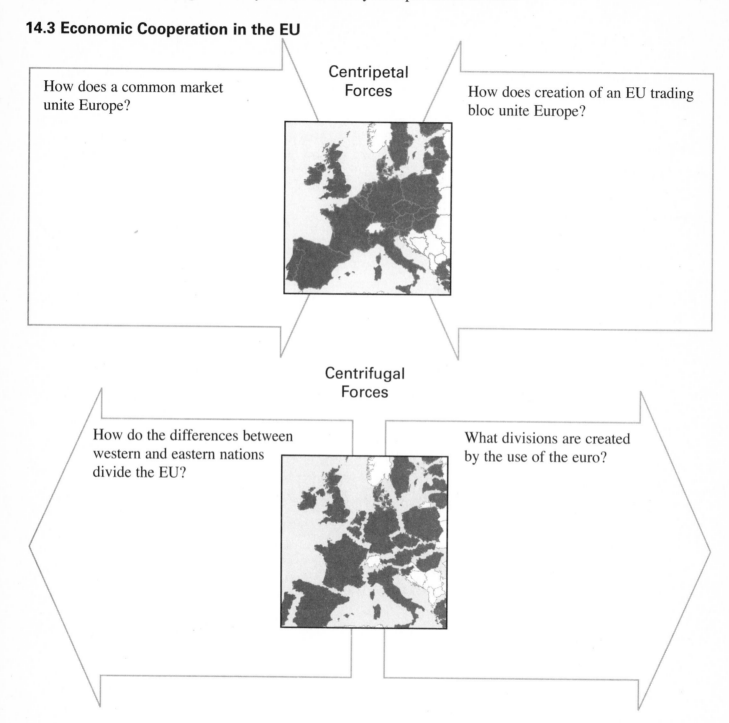

Centripetal Forces

How does a common market unite Europe?

How does creation of an EU trading bloc unite Europe?

Centrifugal Forces

How do the differences between western and eastern nations divide the EU?

What divisions are created by the use of the euro?

What economic centripetal or centrifugal forces did the class experience as it traveled through Europe?

14.4 Political Cooperation in the EU

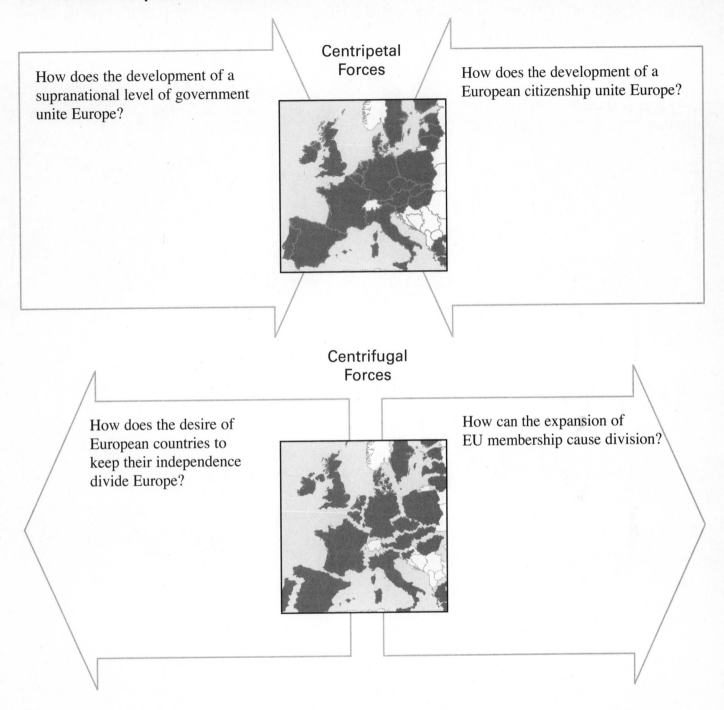

Centripetal Forces

How does the development of a supranational level of government unite Europe?

How does the development of a European citizenship unite Europe?

Centrifugal Forces

How does the desire of European countries to keep their independence divide Europe?

How can the expansion of EU membership cause division?

What political centripetal or centrifugal forces did the class experience as it traveled through Europe?

14.5 Cultural Cooperation in the EU

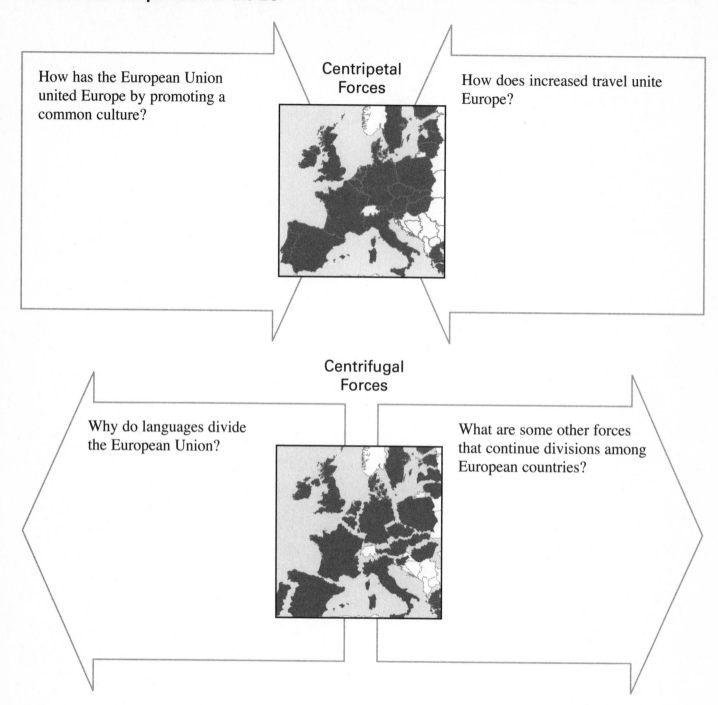

Centripetal Forces

How has the European Union united Europe by promoting a common culture?

How does increased travel unite Europe?

Centrifugal Forces

Why do languages divide the European Union?

What are some other forces that continue divisions among European countries?

What cultural centripetal or centrifugal forces did the class experience as it traveled through Europe?

A simile is a way to compare two things. Follow these steps to compare the European Union to a neighborhood:

1. Complete the statement below. List three similarities between the EU and a neighborhood. An example has been completed for you.

   The European Union is like a neighborhood because

   • the EU's member countries are homes to different cultural groups.

   •

   •

   •

2. Complete the drawing below of the European Union as a neighborhood.

3. Add two details to your drawing to represent two of these terms: *centrifugal force, centripetal force, common market, supranational cooperation.* Label each detail to explain how it represents the term.

A population pyramid shows the size of age groups by sex within a population. Look carefully at the four population pyramids below. They show information about four American cities.

Think about the people who live in each of these cities. Suppose you took a photograph of a group of people in each city. What might they look like? What type of clothing might they be wearing? Your teacher is projecting four photographs. Try to match each one to one of the pyramids below.

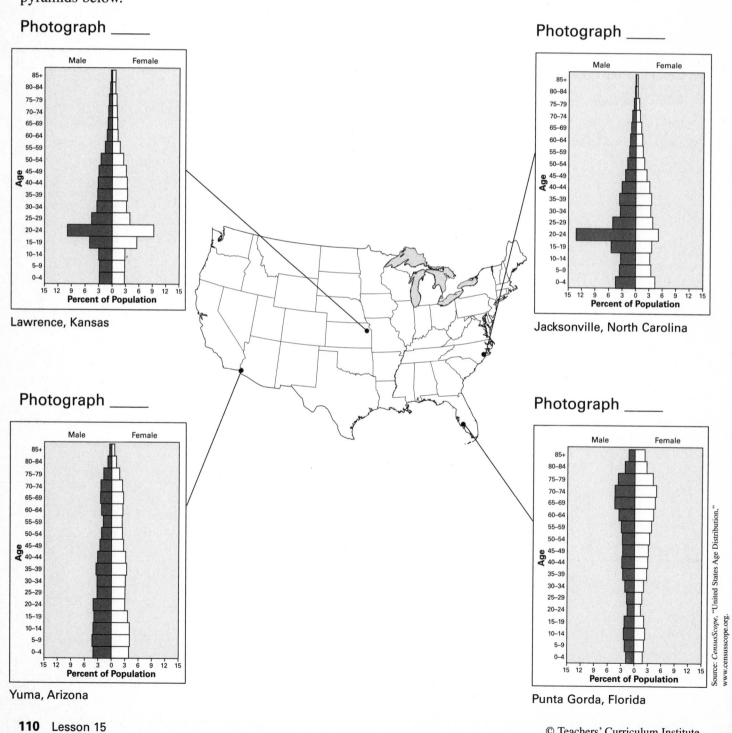

Photograph _____

Lawrence, Kansas

Photograph _____

Jacksonville, North Carolina

Photograph _____

Yuma, Arizona

Photograph _____

Punta Gorda, Florida

Source: *CensusScope*, "United States Age Distribution," www.censusscope.org.

Read Sections 15.1 and 15.2. Then create an illustrated dictionary of the
Geoterms by completing these tasks:

- Create a symbol or an illustration to represent each term.
- Write a definition of each term in your own words.
- Write a sentence that includes the term and the word *Europe*.

Geoterm and Symbol	Definition	Sentence
demography		
dependency ratio		
life expectancy		
replacement rate		
total fertility rate		

Dilemma One: A Shrinking Population

1. As a group, brainstorm at least three answers to this question: *What causes negative population growth?* Write your ideas below.

Italy, 2000

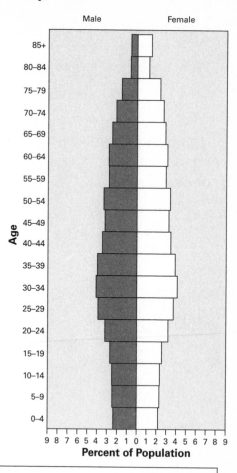

2. Read Section 15.4. Circle any of your ideas that match the causes of negative population growth that you read about. List any additional causes below.

3. Complete this sentence: *Negative population growth can cause problems for a country because...*

Critical Thinking Question 1: *What is the best way to prevent negative population growth?*

4. Rank the plans listed here from strongest (1) to weakest (5). If your group thinks of other ideas, add them to the ranked list. Be prepared to justify your rankings.

5. Read Section 15.5. Then answer these questions in complete sentences: *Which European program for preventing negative population growth do you think is most likely to be successful? Why?*

Plan	Your Rank
A. Provide free childcare to working parents.	_____
B. Allow parents to have paid time off when children are born.	_____
C. Encourage parents to have children earlier in their lives.	_____
D. Pay parents a "birth bonus" for each child they have.	_____
E. Other: _____ _____	_____

Dilemma Two: An Aging Population

1. As a group, brainstorm at least three answers to this question: *What causes a population to age?* Write your ideas below.

2. Read Section 15.6. Circle any of your ideas that match the causes of population aging that you read about. List any additional causes below.

3. Complete this sentence: *Population aging can cause problems for a country because...*

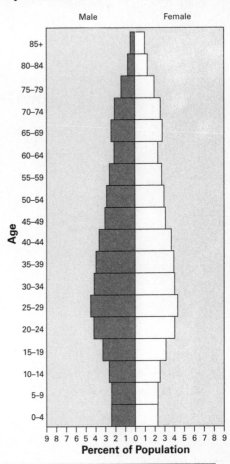

Spain, 2000

Critical Thinking Question 2: *What is the best way to cope with population aging?*

4. Rank the plans listed here from strongest to weakest. If your group thinks of other ideas, add them to the ranked list. Be prepared to justify your rankings.

5. Read Section 15.7. Then answer these questions in complete sentences: *Which European program for coping with population aging do you think is most likely to be successful? Why?*

Plan	Your Rank
A. Require people to save for their own retirement.	_____
B. Give people over 65 a "pension bonus" for each extra year they work.	_____
C. Pay relatives who stay home to help older family members.	_____
D. Encourage companies to pay for health care.	_____
E. Other: _____	_____

Dilemma Three: A Declining Workforce

1. As a group, brainstorm at least two answers to this question: *What causes a workforce to decline?* Write your ideas below.

2. Read Section 15.8. Circle any of your ideas that match the causes of a declining workforce you read about. List any additional causes below.

3. Complete this sentence: *A declining workforce can cause problems for a country because...*

Critical Thinking Question 3: *What is the best way to cope with a declining workforce?*

4. Rank the plans listed here from strongest to weakest. If your group thinks of other ideas, add them to the ranked list. Be prepared to justify your rankings.

5. Read Section 15.9. Then answer these questions in complete sentences: *Which European program for coping with a declining workforce do you think is most likely to be successful? Why?*

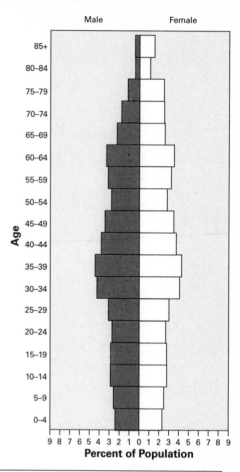

Germany, 2000

Plan	Your Rank
A. Allow workers from other countries to take available jobs.	_____
B. Give mothers paid time off and flexible schedules.	_____
C. Require current workers to work more years before they retire.	_____
D. Move factories to other countries.	_____
E. Other: _____	_____

Use your flipbook of U.S. population pyramids from 1950 through 2050 to answer the questions below.

1. Flip through the U.S. population pyramids from 1950 through 2050. List three interesting things you notice as the bars move.

   •

   •

   •

2. Is the U.S. population aging? Analyze the pyramids in your flipbook to answer this question. Explain your answer in at least two sentences.

3. How can the United States prepare for the demographic changes that are predicted by 2050? Rank the plans listed here from strongest to weakest. If you think of other ideas, add them to the list. Then justify your top two rankings below.

Plan	Your Rank
A. Encourage immigrants to continue to enter the United States.	_____
B. Require baby boomers to work until age 70.	_____
C. Provide government-sponsored childcare for working parents.	_____
D. Pay a $2,000 "medical bonus" to seniors who do not rely on the government for health insurance.	_____
E. Other: _____ _____	_____

Read Sections 16.1 and 16.2. Then create an illustrated dictionary of the Geoterms by completing these tasks:

- Create a symbol or an illustration to represent each term.
- Write a definition of each term in your own words.
- Write a sentence that includes the term and the word *Europe*.

Geoterm and Symbol	Definition	Sentence
acid rain		
nuclear radiation		
river system		
transboundary pollution		

16.3 The Chernobyl Radiation Accident

As you read Section 16.3, complete the map below.

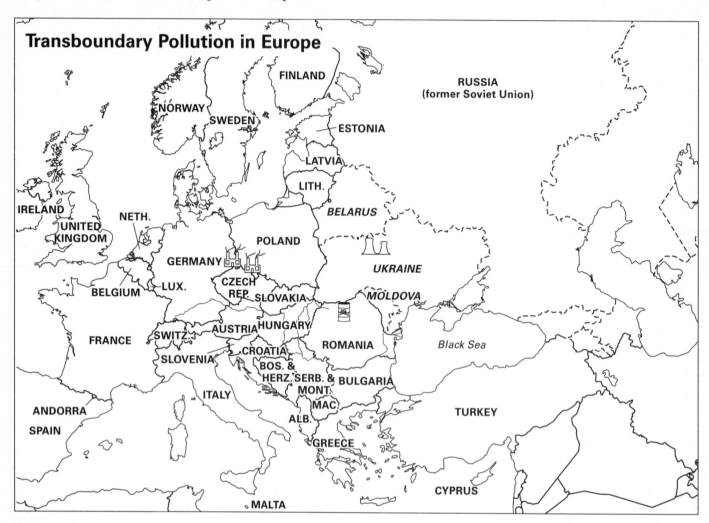

Transboundary Pollution in Europe

Human Error Creates a Deadly Radiation Leak

On the map, color the source of the radioactive pollution. Underline the name of the country where it is located. Then complete this sentence:

Chernobyl became a source of radioactive pollution when…

The Radioactive Cloud Spreads Across Europe

Look at the maps your teacher is projecting. Shade your map to show the spread of radioactive pollution. Circle the names of two countries that were affected by the pollution. Then complete this sentence:

One effect of the spread of radioactive pollution across borders was…

Efforts to Reduce Radioactive Pollution

On the map, draw one effort to reduce radioactive pollution. Then complete this sentence:

_____ *help to reduce radioactive pollution by…*

16.4 The "Black Triangle" and Acid Rain

As you read Section 16.4, complete the map below.

Transboundary Pollution in Europe

Soot from Factories Creates Acid Rain

On the map, color the source of the acid rain. Underline the names of the countries where it is located. Then complete this sentence:

The Black Triangle became a source of acid rain when…

Air Pollution Brings Acid Rain to Other Countries

Look at the map your teacher is projecting. Shade your map to show the pattern of acid rain. Circle the names of two countries affected by acid rain. Then complete this sentence:

One consequence of the spread of acid rain across borders is…

Efforts to Reduce Acid Rain

On the map, draw one effort to reduce acid rain. Then complete this sentence:

_____ *help to reduce acid rain by…*

16.5 The Tisza-Danube Cyanide Spill

As you read Section 16.5, complete the map below.

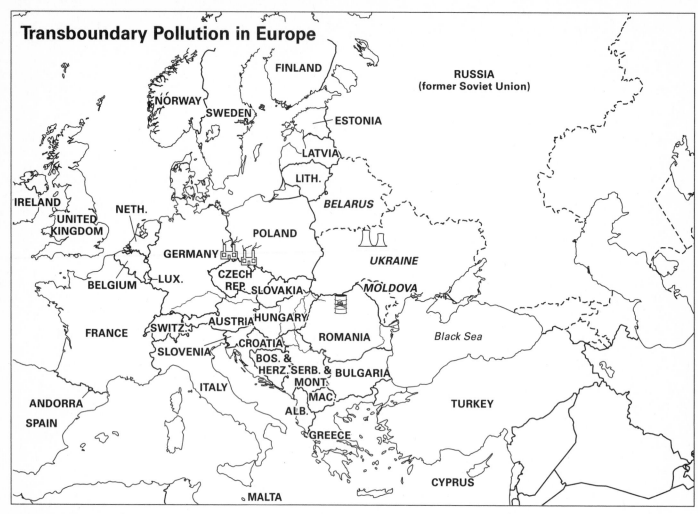

Transboundary Pollution in Europe

A Burst Dam Releases Deadly Chemicals

On the map, color the source of the water pollution. Underline the name of the country where it is located. Then complete this sentence:

Accidental water pollution occurred when…

Cyanide Flows into the Danube River System

Look at the map your teacher is projecting. Shade your map to show the spread of the water pollution. Circle the names of two countries most affected by the pollution. Then complete this sentence:

One consequence of the spread of water pollution across borders was…

Efforts to Reduce Water Pollution

On the map, draw one effort to reduce water pollution. Then complete this sentence:

_____ *help reduce water pollution by…*

Read about another example of transboundary pollution below.
Then follow the directions to complete the map.

Invisible Borders in North America

The map shows how smog spreads across eastern North America. Smog is caused by the burning of fossil fuels in cars, trucks, power plants, and factories. The chemicals produced combine with sunlight to create smog. Smog lowers air quality. It also leads to breathing problems for some people. In Canada, smog season lasts from May to September. As the map shows, much of the smog in Canada comes from the United States.

Smog in Eastern North America

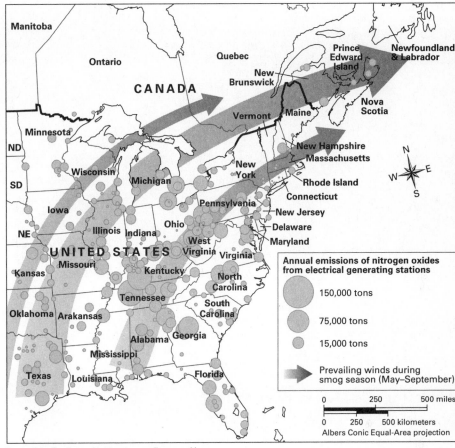

Source: *Canadian Geographic Magazine*, canadiangeographic.ca.

1. Draw a box around the area that is the largest source of the smog. Underline the names of six main states where it is located. Then complete this sentence:

   Smog is caused by...

2. Look at the wind arrows on the map. Shade where you think most of the pollution will spread. Circle the names of four Canadian provinces that will be most affected. Then complete this sentence:

   One consequence of smog spreading across borders is...

3. On the map, draw one possible solution to smog. Then complete this sentence:

   _____ *could help reduce smog by...*

Labeling the Map of Russia

1. Examine the relief map of Russia that your teacher has projected. Shade or draw in the "crumpled" parts of Russia on the map below.

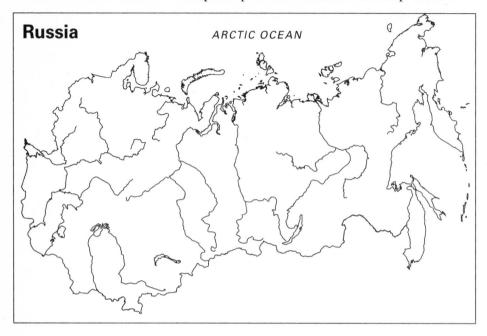

Russia   ARCTIC OCEAN

2. Your teacher will point out the major geographical features of Russia. Label them on your map.

Analyzing the Map of Russia

Think of what you know about land and what causes it to change shape. Look again at the map above and the geographical features you've labeled. Now answer these questions:

3. What are some of the forces that can act upon the land and alter its shape?

4. How might these forces have created some of the geographical features shown on your map?

Read Sections 17.1 and 17.2. Then create an illustrated dictionary of the
Geoterms by completing these tasks:

- Create a symbol or an illustration to represent the term.
- Write a definition of each term in your own words.
- Write a sentence that includes the term and a physical feature
  in Russia.

Geoterm and Symbol	Definition	Sentence
erosion		
glaciation		
physical processes		
tectonic movement		
volcanic activity		

For each of Sections 17.3, 17.5, 17.7, and 17.9, follow these steps:

1. Read the section.

2. Label the diagram that corresponds to the physical process described in that section.

3. Answer the question for that section.

17.3 How Tectonic Movement Shapes Earth

How does tectonic movement affect Earth?

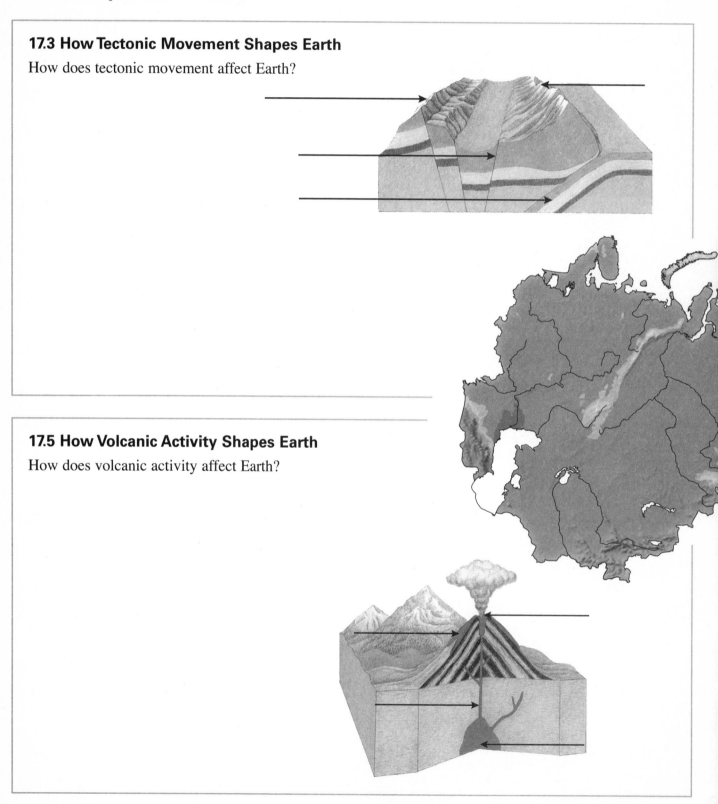

17.5 How Volcanic Activity Shapes Earth

How does volcanic activity affect Earth?

17.7 How Erosion Shapes the Landscape

How does erosion affect the landscape?

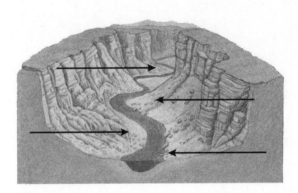

17.9 How Glaciation Shapes the Landscape

How does glaciation affect the landscape?

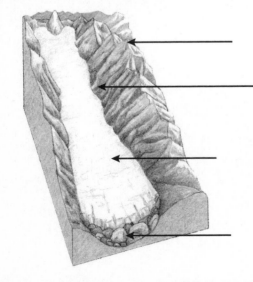

Follow the directions your teacher has projected to complete this part of
your Reading Notes.

Tectonic Movement

Placard letter:
Details you see in the image:

Possible locations of this scene
(numbers from the map):
Actual location:

Placard letter:
Details you see in the image:

Possible locations of this scene
(numbers from the map):
Actual location:

Placard letter:
Details you see in the image:

Possible locations of this scene
(numbers from the map):
Actual location:

Volcanic Activity

Placard letter:
Details from image:

Possible locations of this scene
(numbers from the map):
Actual location:

Placard letter:
Details you see in the image:

Possible locations of this scene
(numbers from the map):
Actual location:

Placard letter:
Details you see in the image:

Possible locations of this scene
(numbers from the map):
Actual location:

Erosion

Placard letter:

Details you see in the image:

Possible locations of this scene
(numbers from the map):

Actual location:

Erosion

Placard letter:

Details you see in the image:

Possible locations of this scene
(numbers from the map):

Actual location:

Placard letter:

Details you see in the image:

Possible locations of this scene
(numbers from the map):

Actual location:

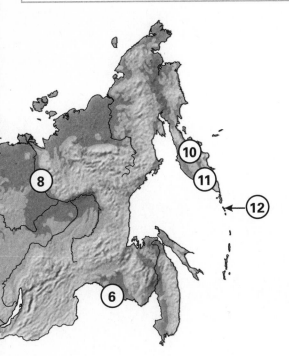

Glaciation

Placard letter:

Details you see in the image:

Possible locations of this scene
(numbers from the map):

Actual location:

Placard letter:

Details you see in the image:

Possible locations of this scene
(numbers from the map):

Actual location:

Placard letter:

Details you see in the image:

Possible locations of this scene
(numbers from the map):

Actual location:

Pretend your teacher has asked you to plan a class field trip to two nearby locations where your class could examine the effects of two physical processes on the land. Complete the steps below as you plan your trip. Use information from your Reading Notes and your own ideas.

1. On the map below, label your hometown or community.

2. Research at least two locations that are within 100 miles of your community. The locations must show evidence of different physical processes. Keep in mind that, although you are looking for examples close to your home, you are also looking for evidence of physical processes that are unique and interesting. Even if this takes you into a nearby state, you want to plan the most enjoyable field trip possible.

3. On the map, label the two locations you have chosen.

4. In the two boxes on the opposite page, sketch what your class might see when they visit each location. Color your drawings.

5. Answer the four questions below each sketch.

The United States

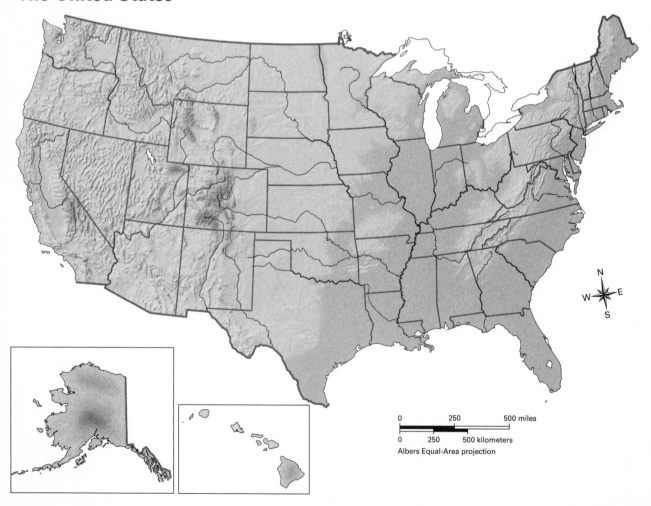

What is this a sketch of?

Which physical process would have shaped
or created this feature?

Why is this feature an example of this
physical process?

How might this physical process affect the
people who live nearby?

What is this a sketch of?

Which physical process would have shaped
or created this feature?

Why is this feature an example of this
physical process?

How might this physical process affect the
people who live nearby?

Part 1

Look at the map your teacher is projecting. Pretend you are a geography student in January 1991. On the map at right, some of the countries are labeled. Label the other country that exists at this time. Then answer the questions.

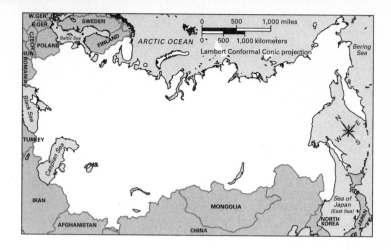

What do you notice about the country on this map?

What might be some advantages to controlling a country this large?

What might be some disadvantages to controlling a country this large?

Part 2

Look at the new map your teacher is projecting. One year has passed. It is now January 1992. On the map at right, draw in and label the countries that now exist in this same region.

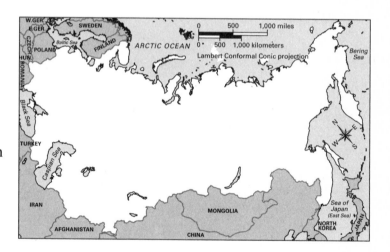

Look at the differences between your two maps. In only one year, the map of this region has changed drastically. What differences do you notice about the second map compared to the first?

What might have happened to cause these changes?

How might the changes in this region affect the people living there?

Read Sections 18.1 and 18.2. Then create an illustrated dictionary of
the Geoterms by completing these tasks:

- Create a symbol or an illustration to represent each term.
- Write a definition of each term in your own words.
- Write a sentence that includes the term.

Geoterm and Symbol	Definition	Sentence
ethnic group		
nation		
nationalism		
nation-state		
state		

18.2 The Geographic Setting

What are the five basic factors that affect the success of a nation-state?

Nation-States of the Former Soviet Union

What are some key ways that a nation-state can keep its people secure?

What is GDP? Along with GDP, what two other factors might indicate whether a nation-state is experiencing economic growth?

How can a government improve its citizens' quality of life? What are two measures of quality of life within a nation-state?

What is nationalism? In what ways can it both foster and work against unity within a nation-state?

What does the organization Freedom House do? What two kinds of rights does it examine for each country?

18.3 Kazakhstan: A Central Asian Giant

1. Complete this scorecard for Kazakhstan. Follow your teacher's directions.

Nation-State Scorecard				
Factors to Consider for Economic Success		**Factors to Consider for Political Success**		
FACTOR	SCORE	FACTOR		SCORE
Location, available resources		Possible ethnic or religious conflict		
GDP growth		Crimes reported		
Poverty		Life expectancy, infant mortality		
Income level		Freedom Index ranking		
Overall success		Overall success		
Comments:		Comments:		

2. Answer these questions:

   Suppose you choose Kazakhstan to host a GeoGames. What is the biggest disadvantage?

   What is the biggest advantage?

3. What *three* new important things have you learned about the political or economic success of Kazakhstan? On the map, draw and label them.

18.4 Azerbaijan: Where Europe Meets Asia

1. Complete this scorecard for Azerbaijan. Follow your teacher's directions.

Nation-State Scorecard				
Factors to Consider for Economic Success		**Factors to Consider for Political Success**		
FACTOR	SCORE	FACTOR		SCORE
Location, available resources		Possible ethnic or religious conflict		
GDP growth		Crimes reported		
Poverty		Life expectancy, infant mortality		
Income level		Freedom Index ranking		
Overall success		Overall success		
Comments:		Comments:		

2. Answer these questions:

   Suppose you choose Azerbaijan to host a GeoGames. What is the biggest disadvantage?

   What is the biggest advantage?

3. What *three* new important things have you learned about the political or economic success of Azerbaijan? On the map, draw and label them.

18.5 Belarus: Between Europe and Russia

1. Complete this scorecard for Belarus. Follow your teacher's directions.

Nation-State Scorecard				
Factors to Consider for Economic Success		**Factors to Consider for Political Success**		
FACTOR	SCORE	FACTOR		SCORE
Location, available resources		Possible ethnic or religious conflict		
GDP growth		Crimes reported		
Poverty		Life expectancy, infant mortality		
Income level		Freedom Index ranking		
Overall success		Overall success		
Comments:		Comments:		

2. Answer these questions:

   Suppose you choose Belarus to host a GeoGames. What is the biggest disadvantage?

   What is the biggest advantage?

3. What *three* new important things have you learned about the political or economic success of Belarus? On the map, draw and label them.

18.6 Lithuania: One of Three Baltic States

1. Complete this scorecard for Lithuania. Follow your teacher's directions.

Nation-State Scorecard				
Factors to Consider for Economic Success		**Factors to Consider for Political Success**		
FACTOR	SCORE	FACTOR	SCORE	
Location, available resources		Possible ethnic or religious conflict		
GDP growth		Crimes reported		
Poverty		Life expectancy, infant mortality		
Income level		Freedom Index ranking		
Overall success		Overall success		
Comments:		Comments:		

2. Answer these questions:

Suppose you choose Lithuania to host a GeoGames. What is the biggest disadvantage?

What is the biggest advantage?

3. What *three* new important things have you learned about the political or economic success of Lithuania? On the map, draw and label them.

18.7 Russia: The Largest Nation on Earth

1. Complete this scorecard for Russia. Follow your teacher's directions.

Nation-State Scorecard				
Factors to Consider for Economic Success		**Factors to Consider for Political Success**		
FACTOR	SCORE	FACTOR	SCORE	
Location, available resources		Possible ethnic or religious conflict		
GDP growth		Crimes reported		
Poverty		Life expectancy, infant mortality		
Income level		Freedom Index ranking		
Overall success		Overall success		
Comments:		Comments:		

2. Answer these questions:

Suppose you choose Russia to host a GeoGames.
What is the biggest disadvantage?

What is the biggest advantage?

3. What *three* new important things have you learned about the political or economic success of Russia? On the map, draw and label them.

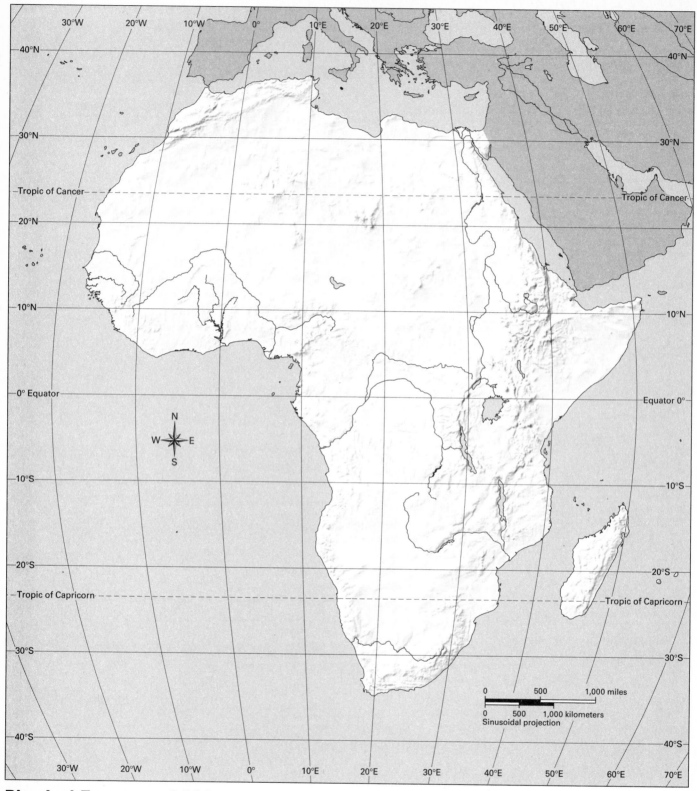

Physical Features of Africa

© Teachers' Curriculum Institute

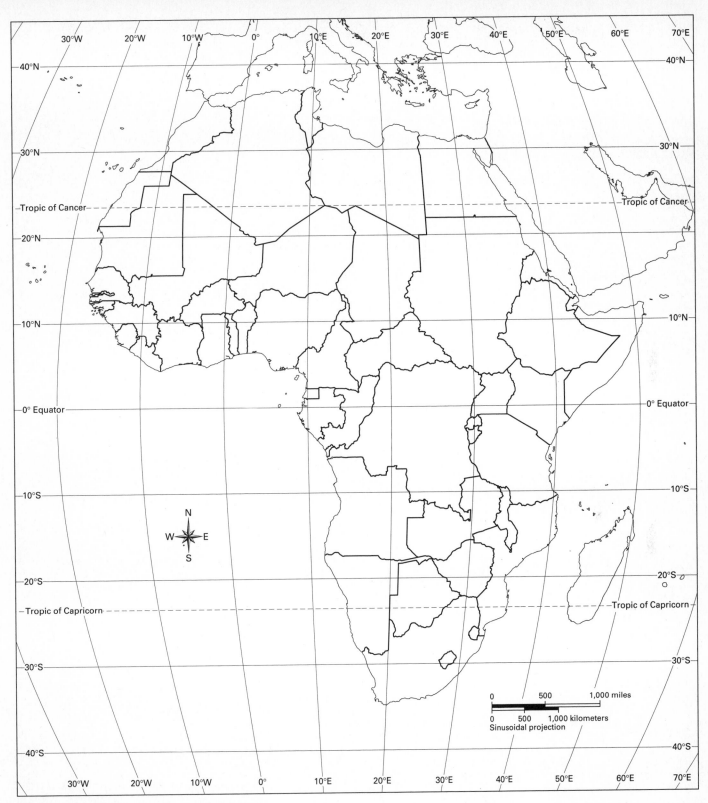

Political Boundaries of Africa

Look carefully at the satellite image and map that your teacher is showing you. On the map, label at least five details about the Nile River.

What questions do you now have about the Nile River? Write at least two questions below.

The Nile River

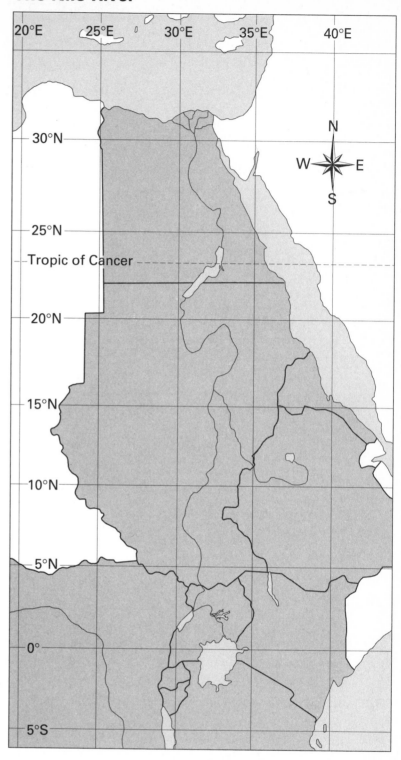

Read Sections 19.1 and 19.2. Then create an illustrated dictionary of the Geoterms by completing these tasks:

- Create a symbol or an illustration to represent each term.
- Write a definition of each term in your own words.
- Write a sentence that includes the term and the words *Nile River*.

Geoterm and Symbol	Definition	Sentence
hydroelectric potential		
perennial irrigation		
river basin		
water cycle		

You will examine 10 features along the Nile River. For each feature, you will make a drawing and write a caption on the map of the Nile. Follow the steps your teacher is projecting to complete your map.

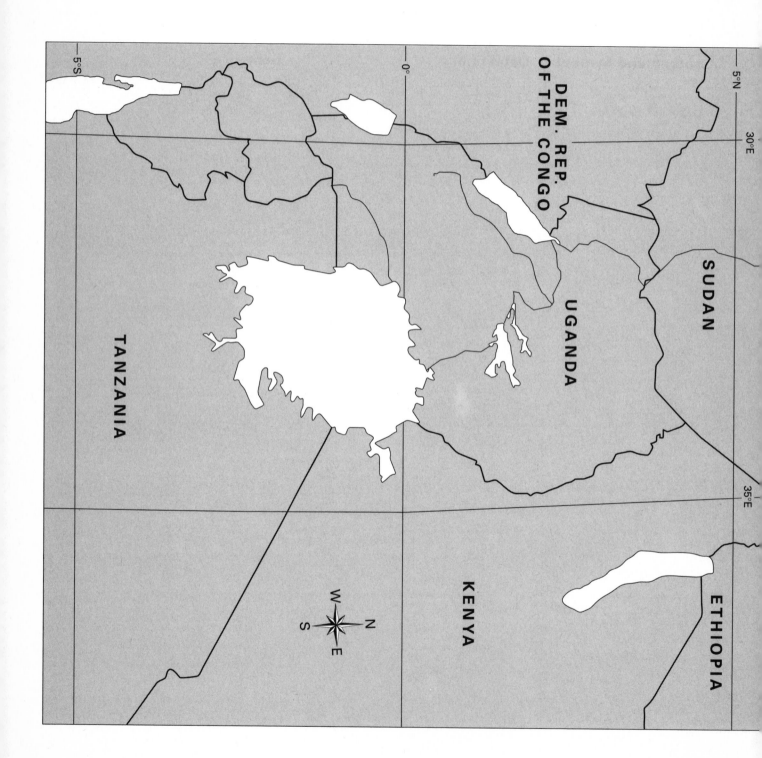

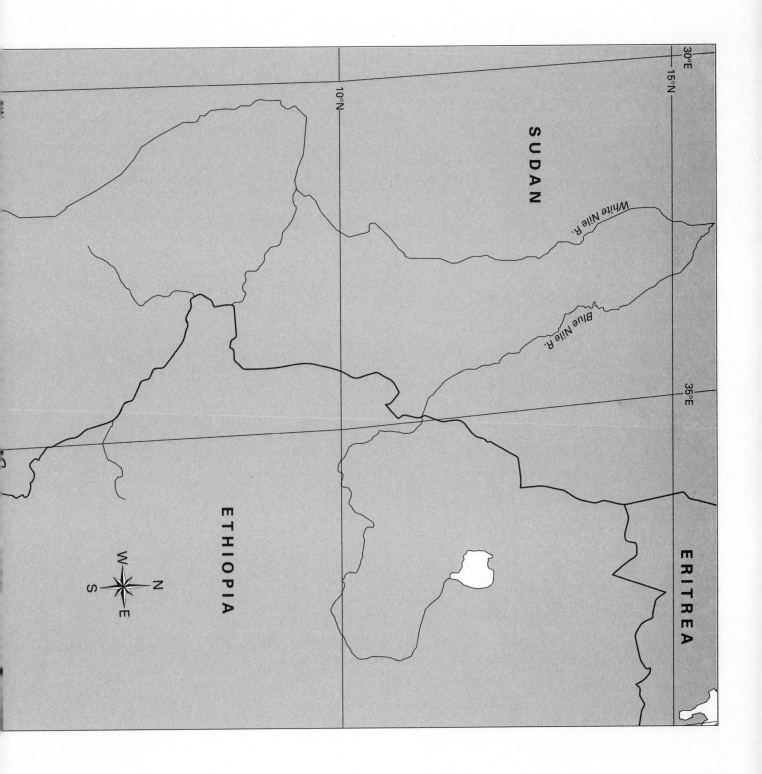

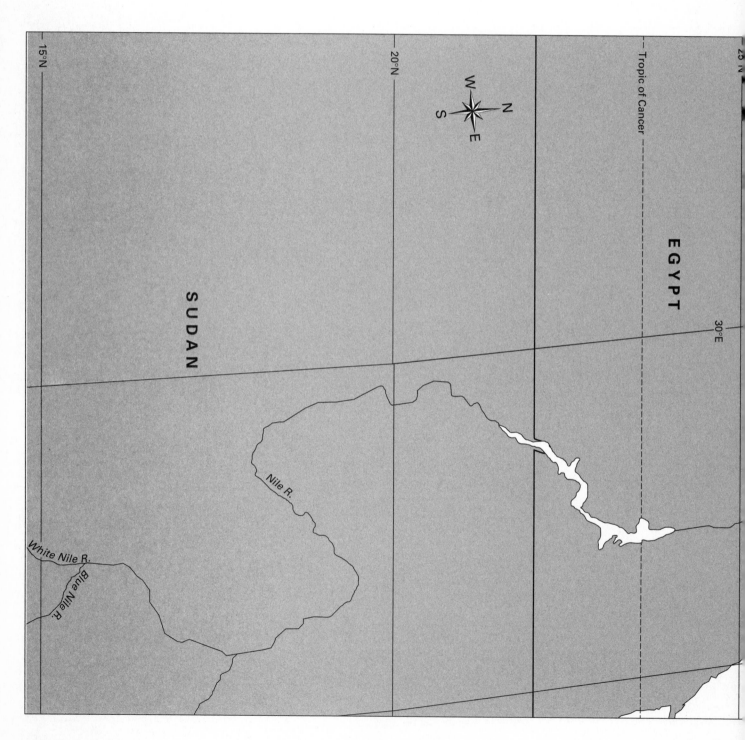

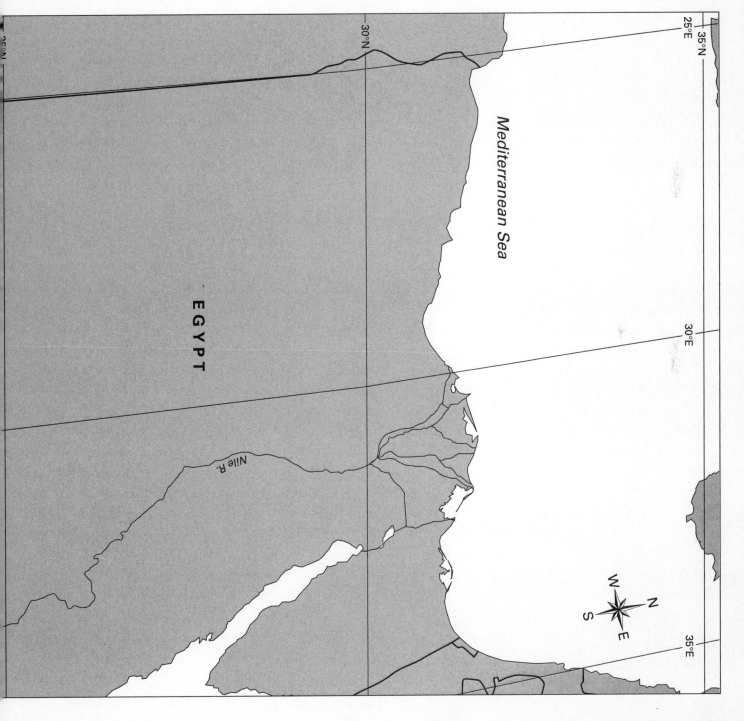

Look back at Preview 19. Write the questions you had about the Nile
River below. Then answer each question in three or four sentences.

Question:

Answer:

Question:

Answer:

Question:

Answer:

Question:

Answer:

1. In the space below, list or draw six things you typically do every day.
   You might include daily routines, such as riding the bus to school.
   Or you might include activities, like going to soccer practice.

2. Now look at the transparency your teacher is projecting.

   • List or draw three details about the physical geography of
     this location.

   • How might your routines and activities change if you lived here?
     Why might they change?

   • How do you think the physical geography of this location influences
     people's routines and activities?

Read Sections 20.1 and 20.2. Then create an illustrated dictionary of the
Geoterms by completing these tasks:

- Create a symbol or an illustration to represent each term.
- Write a definition of each term in your own words.
- Write a sentence that includes the term and the words *desert region*.

Geoterm and Symbol	Definition	Sentence
desertification		
drought		
marginal land		
pastoral nomads		

Follow your teacher's directions to complete the Reading Notes for each of three environments: desert, oasis, and Sahel.

20.3 The Desert Environment

What are the physical characteristics of the desert?

How do you think people have adapted to living in the desert?

20.4 Adaptations to Life in the Desert

How have people adapted to living in the desert?

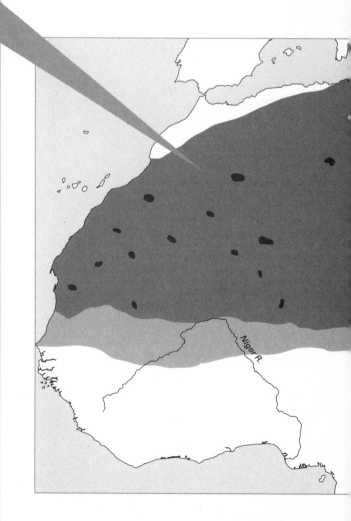

20.5 The Oasis Environment
What are the physical characteristics of oases?

How do you think people have adapted to living in oases?

20.6 Adaptations to Life in the Oases
How have people adapted to living in oases?

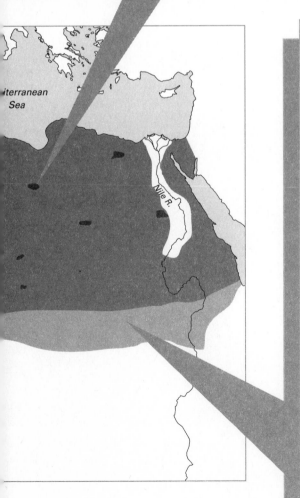

20.7 The Sahel Environment
What are the physical characteristics of the Sahel?

How do you think people have adapted to living in the Sahel?

20.8 Adaptations to Life in the Sahel
How have people adapted to living in the Sahel?

Think about how people have adapted to *your* physical environment. Create a drawing to show your ideas.

1. Draw details of the environment in the background. Think about the physical features, climate, and vegetation of where you live.

2. Draw a person in the center. Add clothing and other possessions to show adaptations people have made. Think about these things:
   • housing
   • transportation
   • economic activity (jobs)
   • the type of community you live in

3. Label ways in which the person has adapted to the environment. For example, you might label a pair of sunglasses "protect eyes from the sun." You might label the person's arms "strong from shoveling snow in the winter."

Carefully examine the image your teacher is projecting. The woman on the cover of this brochure lives in Benin. Benin is a developing country in the western part of Africa. This woman is a *micro-entrepreneur*. That means she has started her own very small business.

Talk about each question with a partner. Then write down your ideas.

- What interesting details do you notice?

- What kind of information or pictures do you think you might see in this pamphlet?

- Women in developing countries in Africa face many challenges. What might some of them be?

- What small business—or *micro-enterprise*—might this woman have created?

- This woman's micro-enterprise affects the lives of her and her family. What might some of those effects be?

- This woman's micro-enterprise also affects individuals and families in her community. What might some of those effects be?

Read Sections 21.1 and 21.2. Then create an illustrated dictionary of the
Geoterms by completing these tasks:

- Create a symbol or an illustration to represent each term.
- Write a definition of each term in your own words.
- Write a sentence that includes the term and the word *Africa* or *women*.

Geoterm and Symbol	Definition	Sentence
gender-based division of labor		
informal economy		
micro-enterprise		
micro-entrepreneur		

Read Section 21.2, and answer the questions for that section. Then, for Sections 21.3, 21.4, and 21.5, read only the section your teacher assigns to you and your partner, and complete that section of Reading Notes.

21.2 The Geographic Setting

What challenges do people in developing countries in Africa face?

What additional challenges do poor African women face as they try to get out of poverty?

21.3 Grinding Peanuts in Rural Mali

The African woman shown here is one of many who created a micro-enterprise. Describe their micro-enterprise, how they created it, and how it works.

How have these micro-entrepreneurs changed people's lives and these women's community?

21.4 Selling in Uganda's "Poor Man's Market"

This African woman created a micro-enterprise. Describe her micro-enterprise, how she created it, and how it works.

How has this micro-entrepreneur changed people's lives and this woman's community?

21.5 Cooking Up Comfort Food in Botswana

The African woman shown here is one of many who created a micro-enterprise. Describe their micro-enterprise, how they created it, and how it works.

How have these micro-entrepreneurs changed people's lives and these women's community?

With your partner, analyze the map below. Talk about the best way to divide Nigeria into three regions. Draw boundaries for the three regions you decide on.

Physical Features of Nigeria

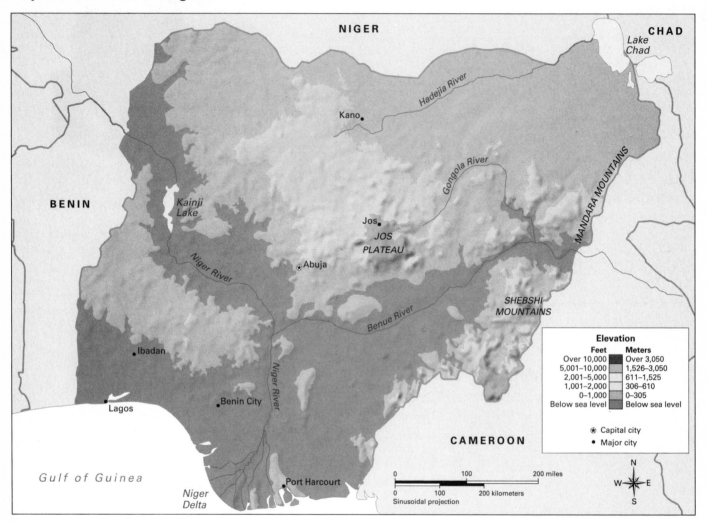

List two reasons you chose the boundaries you did.

1.

2.

© Teachers' Curriculum Institute

Read Sections 22.1 and 22.2. Then create an illustrated dictionary of the
Geoterms by completing these tasks:

- Create a symbol or an illustration to represent each term.
- Write a definition of each term in your own words.
- Write a sentence that includes the term and the word *Nigeria*.

Geoterm and Symbol	Definition	Sentence
colonialism		
cultural region		
ethnic diversity		
linguistic group		

Work with your partner to gather information about Nigeria. You will use the notes you take to design a Web page about Nigeria's three regions. Follow the instructions your teacher has projected.

For each region, read the corresponding section of your book: Section 22.3, 22.4, or 22.5. Fill in the matching row of the table below. List several ideas about each of the four topics. Then have your teacher check your work.

	Physical Environment	Ethnic Groups
Northern Nigeria (Section 22.3)	Photograph ☐	Photograph ☐
Western Nigeria (Section 22.4)	Photograph ☐	Photograph ☐
Eastern Nigeria (Section 22.5)	Photograph ☐	Photograph ☐

Now go to the graphics wall with your partner. At each of the four stations, determine which photograph was taken in the region you are studying. Write the letter of that photograph in the box for the matching topic in that region.

	Culture	Economy
Northern Nigeria (Section 22.3)	Photograph ☐	Photograph ☐
Western Nigeria (Section 22.4)	Photograph ☐	Photograph ☐
Eastern Nigeria (Section 22.5)	Photograph ☐	Photograph ☐

Design the home page for an educational Web site about the regions of Nigeria. Use the three photographs your teacher has given you. Your home page must include these things:

- an appropriate title for the Web site.

- a one-paragraph description of each region in Nigeria. Each paragraph should highlight important features of that region.

- links to other pages on the site. Include at least one link for each region, and title them. For example, a link to the northern region might be called *Life in Northern Nigeria*.

- a caption for each photograph.

- any additional elements, like pop-up ads, links to other sites about Nigeria, and more photographs.

Imagine that your government passed new laws that took away the rights of all people in your ethnic group. People in your ethnic group can no longer vote. They must move into poor-quality housing in rural areas. They cannot to go school with people of other ethnic groups. You are required to carry a passport everywhere you go. You aren't allowed to enter cities unless your passport says you have a job there.

List five ways your life might be different under these new laws.

1.

2.

3.

4.

5.

Read Sections 23.1 and 23.2. Then create an illustrated dictionary of
the Geoterms by completing these tasks:

- Create a symbol or an illustration to represent each term.
- Write a definition of each term in your own words.
- Write a sentence that includes the term and the words *South Africa*.

Geoterm and Symbol	Definition	Sentence
apartheid		
distribution		
multiracial		
segregation		

23.4 Protests Lead to Political Change

Step 1: Read Section 23.4. Look carefully at the picture and graphs in this section. Find at least five pieces of evidence that help prove whether this statement is true or false: *The photograph below fully represents South Africa since the end of apartheid.*

Step 2: Around the photo and graphs below, write any evidence that shows the statement is true. Draw a line to the part of the photo or graphs that illustrates each piece of evidence. An example is done for you.

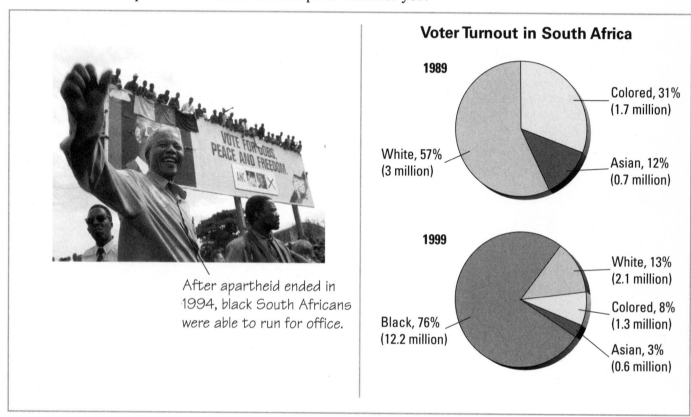

After apartheid ended in 1994, black South Africans were able to run for office.

Voter Turnout in South Africa

1989
Colored, 31% (1.7 million)
White, 57% (3 million)
Asian, 12% (0.7 million)

1999
White, 13% (2.1 million)
Colored, 8% (1.3 million)
Black, 76% (12.2 million)
Asian, 3% (0.6 million)

Step 3: List any evidence that shows the statement is false.

Step 4: In your group, discuss the photograph your teacher is projecting. How well does it represent South Africa today? Record your answer by placing an X on the spectrum below. Then circle two or three pieces of evidence in Steps 2 and 3 that support your position.

not at all representative

somewhat representative

very representative

extremely representative

23.5 South Africa Today: Job Opportunities

Step 1: Read Section 23.5. Look carefully at the picture and graphs in this section. Find at least five pieces of evidence that help prove whether this statement is true or false: *The photograph below fully represents South Africa since the end of apartheid.*

Step 2: Around the photo and graphs below, write any evidence that shows the statement is true. Draw a line to the part of the photo or graphs that illustrates each piece of evidence.

Unemployed South Africans

1987
- Black, 82%
- White, 2%
- Colored, 13%
- Asian, 3%

2001
- Black, 50%
- White, 6%
- Colored, 27%
- Asian, 17%

Step 3: List any evidence that shows the statement is false. An example is done for you.

• Today, blacks, coloreds, and Asians still have much higher unemployment rates than whites.

Step 4: In your group, discuss the photograph your teacher is projecting. How well does it represent South Africa today? Record your answer by placing an X on the spectrum below. Then circle two or three pieces of evidence in Steps 2 and 3 that support your position.

not at all
representative

somewhat
representative

very
representative

extremely
representative

23.6 South Africa Today: Education

Step 1: Read Section 23.6. Look carefully at the picture and graphs in this section. Find at least five pieces of evidence that help prove whether this statement is true or false: *The photograph below fully represents South Africa since the end of apartheid.*

Step 2: Around the photo and graph below, write any evidence that shows the statement is true. Draw a line to the part of the photo or graph that illustrates each piece of evidence. An example is done for you.

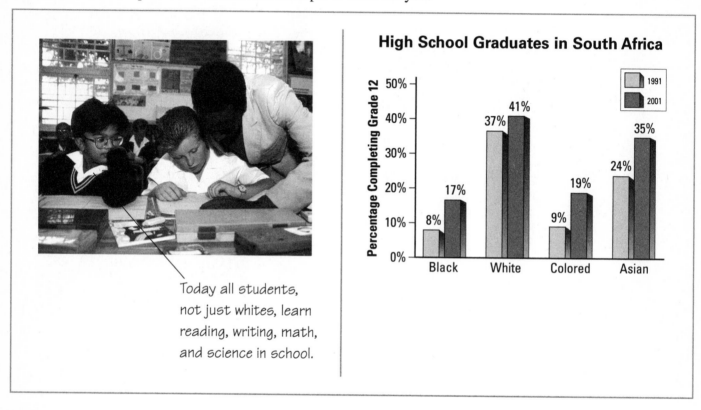

Today all students, not just whites, learn reading, writing, math, and science in school.

High School Graduates in South Africa

Percentage Completing Grade 12

1991
2001

Black: 8%, 17%
White: 37%, 41%
Colored: 9%, 19%
Asian: 24%, 35%

Step 3: List any evidence that shows the statement is false.

Step 4: In your group, discuss the photograph your teacher is projecting. How well does it represent South Africa today? Record your answer by placing an X on the spectrum below. Then circle two or three pieces of evidence in Steps 2 and 3 that support your position.

not at all
representative

somewhat
representative

very
representative

extremely
representative

23.7 South Africa Today: Living Conditions

Step 1: Read Section 23.7. Look carefully at the picture and graphs in this section. Find at least five pieces of evidence that help prove whether this statement is true or false: *The photograph below fully represents South Africa since the end of apartheid.*

Step 2: Around the photo and graphs below, write any evidence that shows the statement is true. Draw a line to the part of the photo or graphs that illustrates each piece of evidence. An example is done for you.

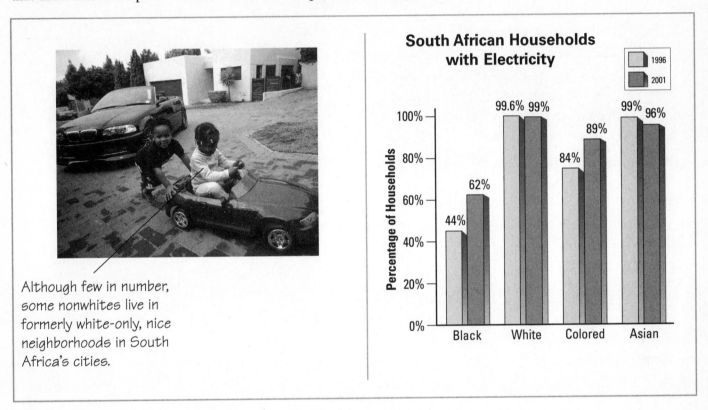

Although few in number, some nonwhites live in formerly white-only, nice neighborhoods in South Africa's cities.

South African Households with Electricity

1996
2001

Percentage of Households

100% 99.6% 99%   99% 96%
           84% 89%
80%
       62%
60%
44%
40%

20%

0%
      Black   White   Colored   Asian

Step 3: List any evidence that shows the statement is false.

Step 4: In your group, discuss the photograph your teacher is projecting. How well does it represent South Africa today? Record your answer by placing an X on the spectrum below. Then circle two or three pieces of evidence in Steps 2 and 3 that support your position.

| not at all representative | somewhat representative | very representative | extremely representative |

Review the four categories listed on the rating card below. Think about whether South Africa has made progress in each area. If so, how much progress has been made?

Using information from your Reading Notes, fill in the card for South Africa's progress. Give South Africa a rating for each area. Use the rating scale to help you. Then write two or three sentences to explain each rating. Include details from your Reading Notes to support the rating.

Rating Scale

1	has made excellent progress toward equality for all ethnic groups
2	has made good progress toward equality, but still has a way to go before all ethnic groups have equality
3	has made some progress, but much more progress is needed before all ethnic groups have equality
4	has made almost no progress toward equality
5	South Africans are worse off now than during apartheid

Rating Card for the New South Africa

Area	Rating	Reasoning
Political opportunities		
Job opportunities		
Educational opportunities		
Living conditions		

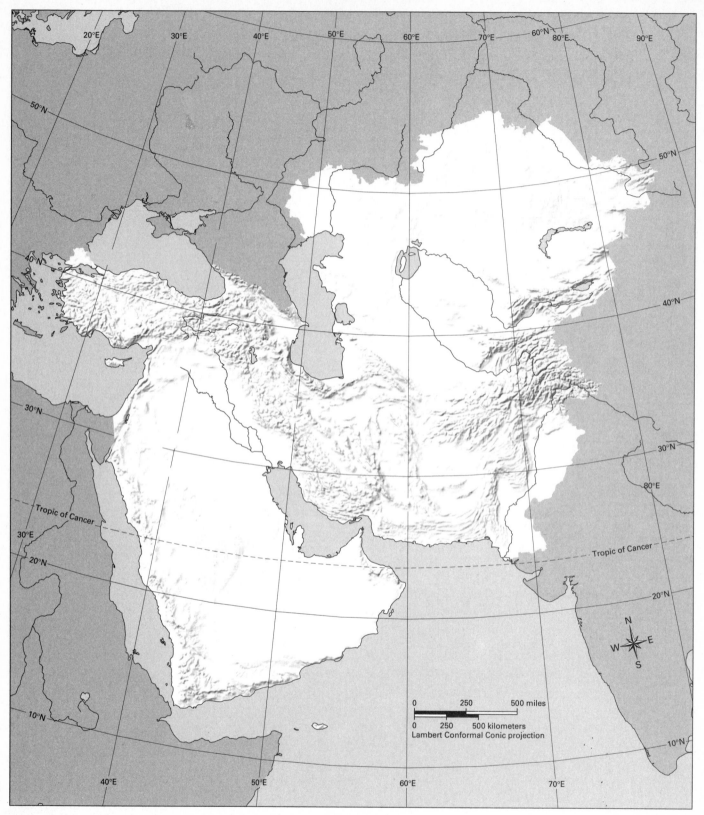

Physical Features of Southwest and Central Asia

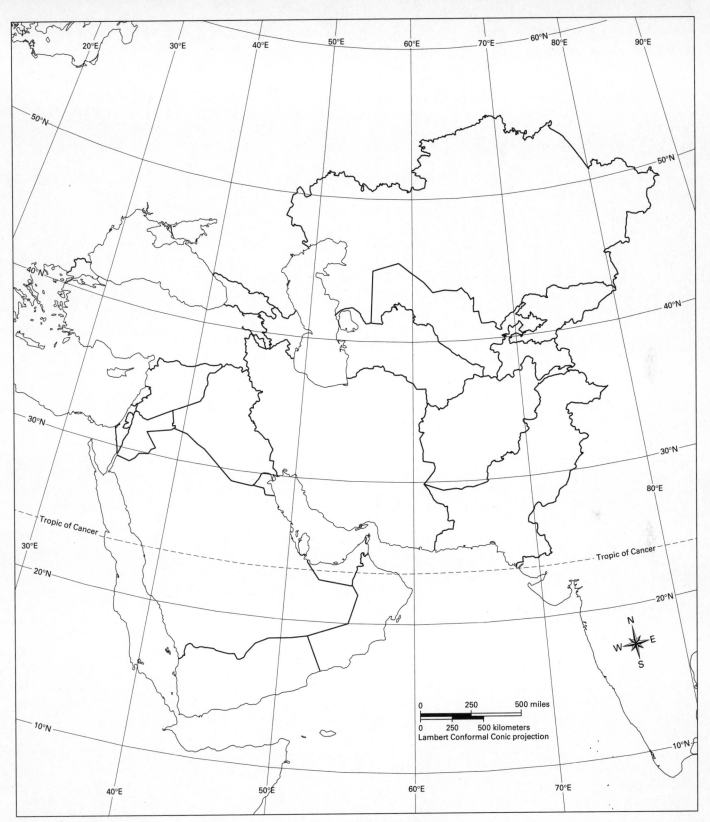

Political Boundaries of Southwest and Central Asia

How might having a lot of oil affect Southwest Asia? List at least three ways you think this resource might affect the people and places in this region. An example is done for you.

- This resource might provide jobs for many people.

Read Sections 24.1 and 24.2. Then create an illustrated dictionary of the
Geoterms by completing these tasks:

- Create a symbol or an illustration to represent each term.
- Write a definition of each term in your own words.
- Write a sentence that includes the term and the words *Southwest Asia*.

Geoterm and Symbol	Definition	Sentence
crude oil		
nonrenewable resource		
oil reserves		
renewable resource		

Oil in Southwest Asia: How "Black Gold" Has Shaped a Region

24.3 The Geology and Geography of Oil

Read Section 24.3. Then, on the map, rank each of Southwest Asia's oil countries according to the size of its proven oil reserves. Label them from 1 (largest reserve) to 10 (smallest reserve). Shade the three countries with the largest oil reserves.

Southwest Asia: Who Has the Oil?

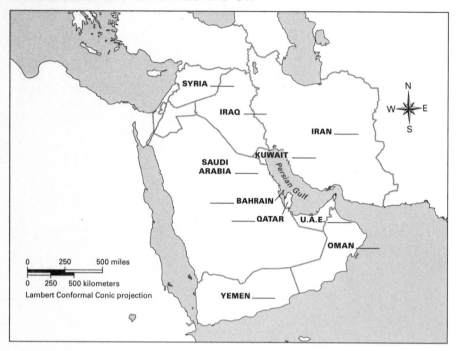

Answer these questions:

• How does oil form? Explain the process in at least three steps.

• Why is so much oil buried under Southwest Asia?

• Are oil reserves distributed equally among the countries of Southwest Asia? Explain.

24.4 Oil Wealth and People's Well-Being

Read Section 24.4. Then, on the map, rank each of Southwest Asia's oil countries according to its Human Development Index (HDI) rank. Label them from 1 (highest rank) to 10 (lowest rank). Shade the three countries with the highest HDI ranks.

Southwest Asia: Measuring Well-Being with HDI

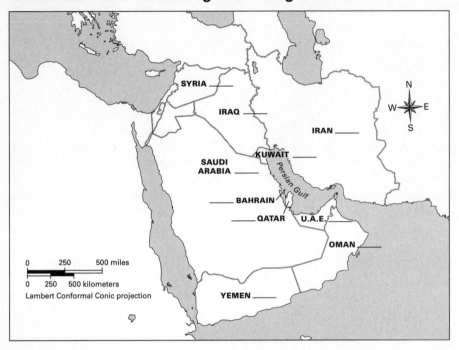

Answer these questions:

- How has oil made the people of Southwest Asia better off?

- Why isn't per capita GDP always an accurate reflection of people's wealth?

- What are some examples of why some oil countries haven't been able to end poverty?

24.5 The Price and Flow of Oil

Read Section 24.5. Then, on the map, place an X on the lines for the countries that are OPEC members. Circle the names of the Southwest Asian countries who were top contributors to the costs of the Persian Gulf War.

Southwest Asia: OPEC Members and Persian Gulf War Contributors

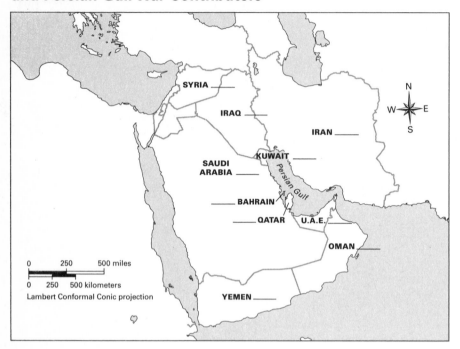

Answer these questions:

- What have been the goals of Southwest Asian OPEC members?

- What two realities have limited OPEC's power?

- What were the two types of coalition members in the Persian Gulf War? Why were they coalition members?

Explain the title of Chapter 24 by adding to the map below.

- Around the map, write at least three sentences explaining how oil has affected Southwest Asia.

- Your sentences should mention at least three countries in Southwest Asia.

- Your sentences should use at least three of this chapter's Geoterms: *crude oil, nonrenewable resource, oil reserves,* and *renewable resource.*

- Connect each sentence to a specific part of the map with a line.

An example is done for you.

Oil in Southwest Asia: How "Black Gold" Has Shaped a Region

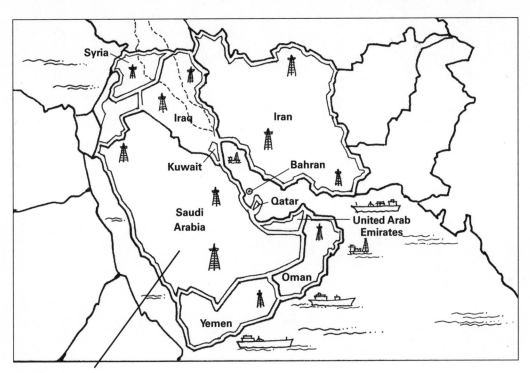

Saudi Arabia has the largest known oil reserves in Southwest Asia.

Read Sections 25.1 and 25.2. Then create an illustrated dictionary of the
Geoterms by completing these tasks:

- Create a symbol or an illustration to represent each term.
- Write a definition of each term in your own words.
- Write a sentence that includes the term and the word *Istanbul*.

Geoterm and Symbol	Definition	Sentence
capital city		
primate city		
site		
situation		

For each of Sections 25.3, 25.4, and 25.5, list features of primate cities on the left and comparisons to the trading game on the right. An example is done for you.

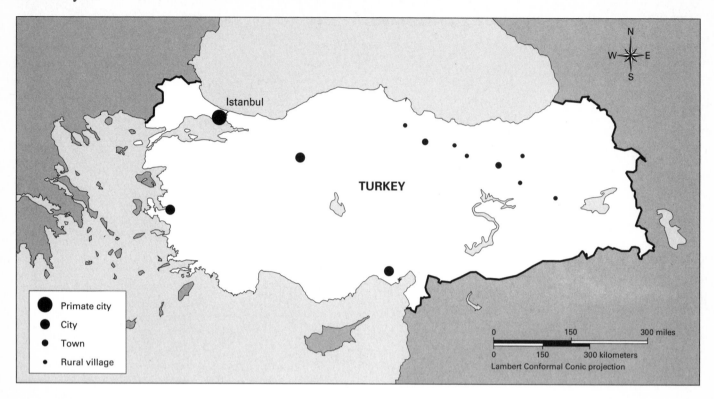

25.3 A Country's Largest City by Far

Features of Primate Cities	Features of the Trading Game
• A primate city's population is at least twice that of the next largest city in the country. Istanbul has more than twice the population of Ankara.	• By the end of the game, the desks representing the primate city in Country 2 had the most students near them.

25.4 A Center of Economic Power

Features of Primate Cities	Features of the Trading Game

25.5 A Center of National Life and Culture

Features of Primate Cities	Features of the Trading Game

Primate cites are found in states as well as in countries. Does your state have a primate city? Follow these steps to find out:

1. Find the population of the two largest cities in your state.

2. Multiply the population of the second largest city by 2.

3. Is the population of the largest city more than twice the population of the second largest city? If so, your state has a primate city.

Now create a map of your state.

- Draw your state in the box.

- If your state has a primate city, place a dot on the map for it. Label it. If not, label what you think is your state's most important city. It may be the largest city or the capital city.

- Describe your state's most important city by completing these sentences:

  One advantage of the location of this city is

  This city is a center of power because

  This city reflects my state's culture by

- Add pictures to your map to illustrate each sentence.

Map of My State

Step 1: Examine the image your teacher has projected. Then answer these questions:

1. From where do you think this image was taken?

2. What do you think this image shows?

3. This was taken in 1964. Would you expect this area to look any different if the image were taken today? In what ways?

Step 2: Examine the second image your teacher has projected. Then answer these questions:

1. What does the dashed red line represent?

2. What might have happened to explain the differences between the two images?

3. How might the lives of people living near the Aral Sea—like farmers, fishing crews, and factory workers—be affected by this change?

Read Sections 26.1 and 26.2. Then create an illustrated dictionary of the
Geoterms by completing these tasks:

- Create a symbol or an illustration to represent each term.
- Write a definition of each term in your own words.
- Write a sentence that includes the term and the words *Aral Sea*.

Geoterm and Symbol	Definition	Sentence
environmental degradation		
groundwater		
salinization		
water stress		

Read each indicated part of Sections 26.3, 26.4, and 26.5. Then answer
the related question.

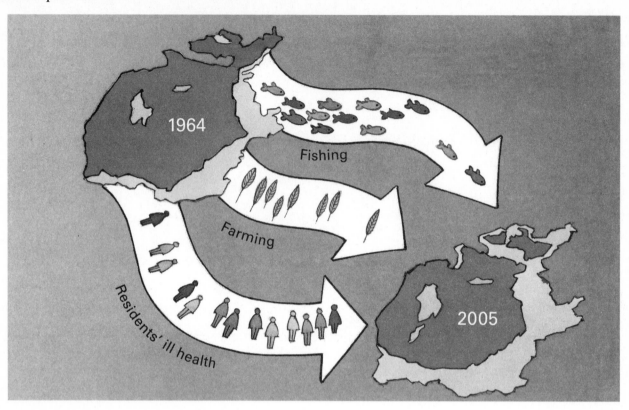

26.3 The Shrinking Sea and Farming

Read Section 26.3 up to "Salinization Creates a New Desert." Then answer this question: *What was life like for farmers in the Aral Sea region when cotton was king?*	Read the rest of Section 26.3. Then answer this question: *How have farmers been affected by the shrinking Aral Sea?*

26.4 The Shrinking Sea and Fishing

Read Section 26.4 up to "The Collapse of the Aral Sea Fishing Industry." Then answer this question: *What was life like for people in the fishing industry when the sea was rich in fish?*

Read the rest of Section 26.4. Then answer this question: *How was the fishing industry affected by the shrinking Aral Sea?*

26.5 The Shrinking Sea and Quality of Life

Read Section 26.5 up to "Pollution Damages the Health of Residents." Then answer this question: *What was life like for people of the Aral Sea region when water was plentiful?*

Read the rest of Section 26.5. Then answer this question: *How has people's health been affected by the shrinking Aral Sea?*

Americans use over 400 billion gallons of water per day. More than 135 billion gallons are used for irrigation daily. The average American uses about 180 gallons of water every day for cooking, washing, drinking, and watering. That's a lot of water! But where does it come from?

Step 1: Use one of these sources to find one fact about where the water in your home comes from:

- a parent or guardian
- a water department employee
- a city employee
- the Internet

Write what you discover below. Be prepared to share what you learn.

Step 2: Trace the water that comes from the faucet in your home or school back to its source. Use the information you and your classmates have gathered. Draw a simple map that connects the faucet below with the source of your water. Label the important details of your map. Provide a key to explain any symbols you use.

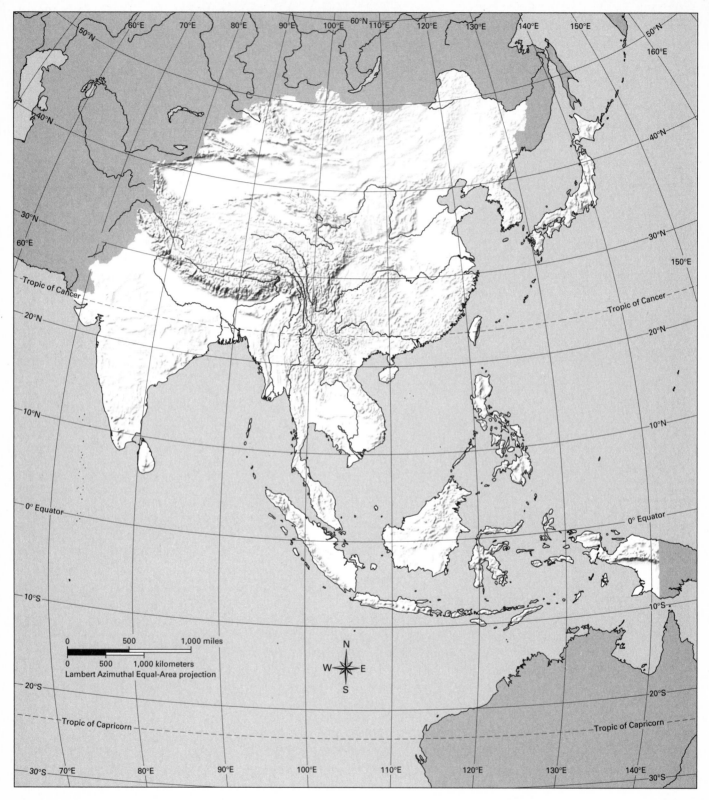

Physical Features of Monsoon Asia

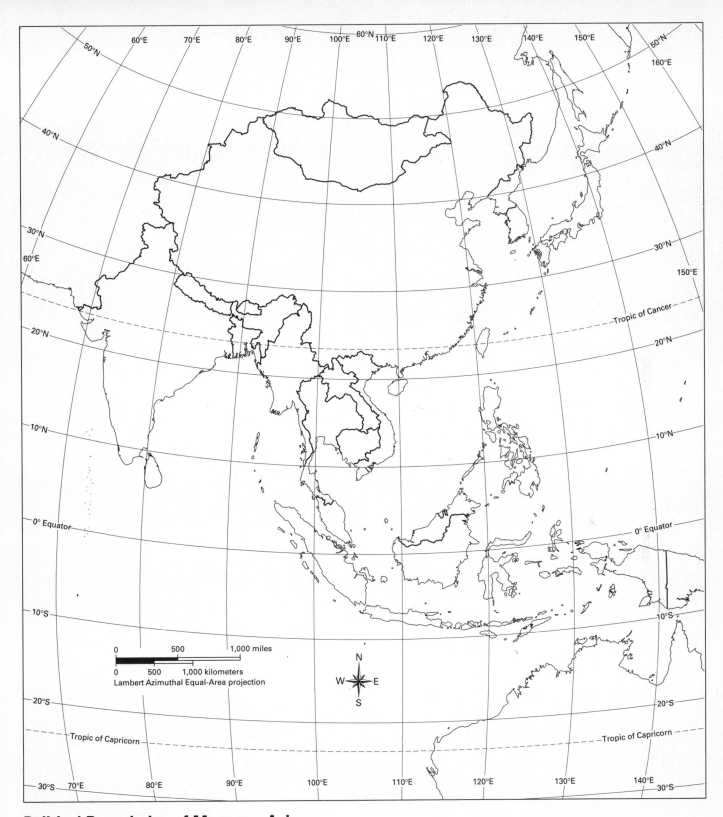

Political Boundaries of Monsoon Asia

Look carefully at the climagraph of Mumbai, India.
What is the wettest month or months in Mumbai?

What is the driest month or months in Mumbai?

What effects might this city's climate have on the people who live here?

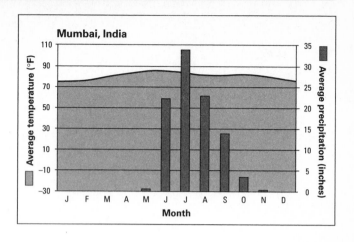

Look carefully at the table of climate zones below. Which of these climate zones do you think Mumbai might be in? Why?

World Climate Zones

Climate Zone	Definition
ice cap	very cold all year with permanent ice and snow
tundra	very cold winters, cold summers, and little rain or snow
subarctic	cold, snowy winters and cool, rainy summers
highlands	temperature and precipitation vary with latitude and elevation
marine west coast	warm summers, cool winters, and rainfall all year
humid continental	warm, rainy summers and cool, snowy winters
Mediterranean	warm all year with dry summers and short, rainy winters
humid subtropical	hot, rainy summers and mild winters with some rain
semiarid	hot, dry summers and cool, dry winters
arid	hot and dry all year with very little rain
tropical wet and dry	hot all year with rainy and dry seasons
tropical wet	hot and rainy all year

Read Sections 27.1 and 27.2. Then create an illustrated dictionary of
the Geoterms by completing these tasks:

• Create a symbol or an illustration to represent each term.

• Write a definition of each term in your own words.

• Write a sentence that includes the term.

Geoterm and Symbol	Definition	Sentence
atmospheric pressure		
monsoon		
orographic effect		
rain shadow		

27.3 The Wet Months in Dhaka, Bangladesh (24°N, 90°E)

Follow these steps to complete the Reading Notes for Section 27.3:

1. When you have assembled your puzzle for Dhaka correctly, read Section 27.3.

2. As you read the subsection "One of the World's Wettest Capitals," look for details about Dhaka's climate. Write a caption below your climagraph that summarizes that climate.

3. As you read "Life Depends on the Rain," look for more *effects of* and *adaptations to* this climate. Add them to the list below.

Paste climate map here.

Paste climagraph here.

Paste photograph here.

Paste list of effects and adaptations here.

27.4 The Dry Months of Jodhpur, India (26°N, 73°E)

Follow these steps to complete the Reading Notes for Section 27.4:

1. When you have assembled your puzzle for Jodhpur correctly, read Section 27.4.

2. As you read the subsection "A City on the Edge of a Desert," look for details about Jodhpur's climate. Write a caption below your climagraph that summarizes that climate.

3. As you read "Water Is a Critical Resource," look for more effects of and adaptations to this climate. Add them to the list below.

Paste climate map here.

Paste climagraph here.

Paste photograph here.

Paste list of effects and adaptations here.

27.5 Waiting for the Rains in Calcutta, India (23°N, 88°E)

Follow these steps to complete the Reading Notes for Section 27.5:

1. When you have assembled your puzzle for Calcutta correctly, read Section 27.5.

2. As you read the subsection "Wet Summers and Dry Winters," look for details about Calcutta's climate. Write a caption below your climagraph that summarizes that climate.

3. As you read "Monsoon Rains Begin and End Life," look for more effects of and adaptations to this climate. Add them to the list below.

Paste climate map here.

Paste climagraph here.

Paste photograph here.

Paste list of effects and adaptations here.

27.6 Living in the Rain Shadow: Pune, India (19°N, 74°E)

Follow these steps to complete the Reading Notes for Section 27.6:

1. When you have assembled your puzzle for Pune correctly, read Section 27.6.

2. As you read the subsection "A Year-Round Dry Climate," look for details about Pune's climate. Write a caption below your climagraph that summarizes that climate.

3. As you read "Limited Rainfall Makes Water Precious," look for more effects of and adaptations to this climate. Add them to the list below.

Paste climate map here.

Paste climagraph here.

Paste photograph here.

Paste list of effects and adaptations here.

What Effect Does Climate Have on Your Life?

Step 1: Fill in the table with monthly rainfall amounts and temperatures for your town or a city near you. Use the data your teacher gives you, or research your own.

	Jan	Feb	Mar	Apr	May	Jun	Jul	Aug	Sep	Oct	Nov	Dec
Average Rainfall (inches)												
Average Temperature (°F)												

Step 2: Create a climagraph for your hometown or a city near you.

- Using the axis on the right side of the graph, plot the average rainfall for January. Draw a bar above the first "J" up to the amount of rainfall for that month. Do the same for the next 11 months.

- Using the axis on the left side of the graph, plot the average temperature for January. Place a dot over the "J" at the average temperature for that month. Do the same for the next 11 months. Then connect the dots.

Step 3: Answer these questions:

- What are the warmest months in your town? Circle them on the climagraph.

- What are the coolest months in your town? Draw a square around them on the climagraph.

- What are the wettest months in your town? Draw a triangle around them.

- What are two effects that climate has on human activity in your town?

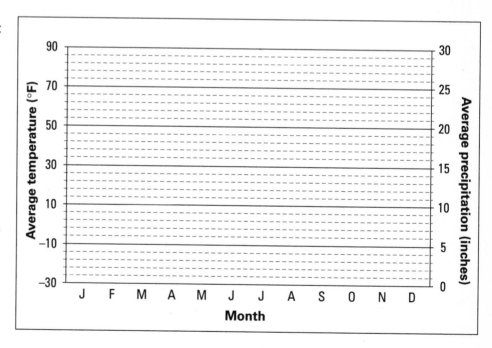

- What is one way people in your town have adapted to this climate?

© Teachers' Curriculum Institute

With your partner, follow these steps:

1. Quickly review the information in the table below. Make sure you understand what each heading means.

Workers Around the World, 2002

Country	Total Number of Workers	Average Level of English Skill	Average Annual Salary of IT Programmers (in U.S. dollars)
Bulgaria	3.9 million	good	$3,600–$6,000
Canada	16 million	good	$28,000
China	734.3 million	poor	$9,000
India	439 million	good	$5,900
Ireland	1.8 million	good	$23,000–$34,000
Israel	2.4 million	good	$15,000–$38,000
Pakistan	40 million	good	$3,600–$6,000
Philippines	32 million	good	$6,600
Russia	72.6 million	poor	$5,000–$7,500
Thailand	33.2 million	poor	$11,100
Ukraine	22.8 million	poor	$5,000–$11,700

Source: "A Buyer's Guide to Offshore Outsourcing," *CIO Magazine*, Nov. 15, 2002.

2. Fill in the map key below. Use one color for the top item in each category. Use a second color for the bottom item in the each category.

Total Number of Workers	Average Level of English Skill	Average Annual Salary of IT Programmers
☐ 50 million and up ☐ below 50 million	☐ good ☐ poor	☐ under $12,000 ☐ $12,000 and up

3. Follow the directions next to each map on the opposite page. Then answer this question: *In recent years, American companies have sent many IT jobs to other countries. Analyze your three maps. To which country do you think most of these jobs are being sent? Why?*

Workers Around the World

Color the countries with 50 million workers or more. Then color those with fewer than 50 million workers. Use the colors from the key on the previous page.

Average English Skill of Workers

Color the countries that have workers with a good level of English skill. Then color those that have a poor level of English skill. Use the colors from the key on the previous page.

Average Annual Salaries of IT Programmers

Color the countries in which the average salary for IT workers is less than $12,000. Then color those in which the average salary is $12,000 or more. Use the colors from the key on the previous page.

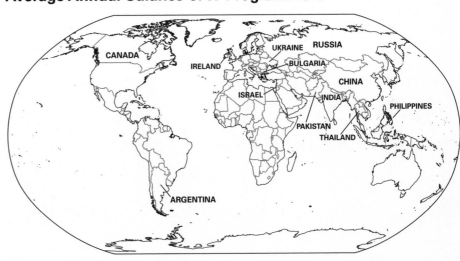

Read Sections 28.1 and 28.2. Then create an illustrated dictionary of the
Geoterms by completing these tasks:

- Create a symbol or an illustration to represent each term.
- Write a definition of each term in your own words.
- Write a sentence that includes the term and the word *India*.

Geoterm and Symbol	Definition	Sentence
comparative advantage		
information technology		
outsource		
time zone		

28.3 Advantage Factor One: Low Wages

Step 1: Read Section 28.3, and answer these questions:

- What are two reasons why wages for workers in India are lower than in many other countries?

- Why do Indian workers want IT jobs?

- List one interesting statistic about low wages in India.

Step 2: Visit an Internet search station. Conduct a search for information about the first person you will interview (read the handout on the wall). Take notes below.

Internet Search Notes
Name of IT worker:
Occupation:
Salary:
Interesting facts about this IT worker:

Step 3: Attend the online meeting, and take notes below.

Online Meeting Notes
U.S. time of meeting: _____ A.M./P.M.
Question for this IT worker: *How has the IT revolution affected you and other people who work in the IT industry?*

List three ways the IT revolution has affected Meena and other Indian workers.

28.4 Advantage Factor Two: English Speakers

Step 1: Read Section 28.4, and answer these questions:

- Why is English widely spoken in India?

- How do English skills give Indians an advantage in the IT industry?

- List one interesting statistic about English speakers in India.

Step 2: Visit an Internet search station. Conduct a search for information about the second person you will interview. Take notes below.

Internet Search Notes
Name of IT worker:
Occupation:
Salary:
Interesting facts about this IT worker:

Step 3: Attend the online meeting, and take notes below.

Online Meeting Notes
U.S. time of meeting: _____ A.M./P.M.

Question for this IT worker: *How has the IT revolution affected you and other people who work outside of the IT industry?*

List three ways the IT revolution has affected this worker and others.

28.5 Advantage Factor Three: Trained Workers

Step 1: Read Section 28.5, and answer these questions:

- Why does India lead in technical education?

- Why don't all Indians have an equal opportunity for education?

- List one interesting statistic about India's trained workers.

Step 2: Visit an Internet search station. Conduct a search for information about the third person you will interview. Take notes below.

Internet Search Notes
Name of IT worker:
Occupation:
Salary:
Interesting facts about this IT worker:

Step 3: Attend the online meeting, and take notes below.

Online Meeting Notes
U.S. time of meeting: _____ A.M./P.M.
Question for this IT worker: *How has the IT revolution affected you and other highly educated people in the IT industry?*

List three ways the IT revolution has affected this worker and others.

If you were given the opportunity to visit any place in the world, where would you visit?

Why would you like to visit this place?

What clothing and supplies would you need to be prepared to visit this place? In the backpack, draw and label three of the most important items you would need.

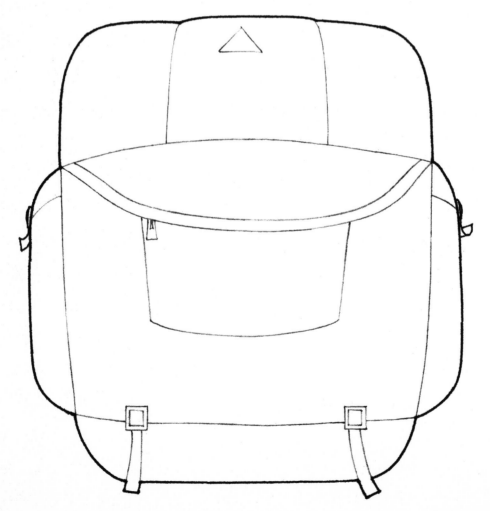

Read Sections 29.1 and 29.2. Then create an illustrated dictionary of the
Geoterms by completing these tasks:

- Create a symbol or an illustration to represent each term.
- Write a definition of each term in your own words.
- Write a sentence that includes the term and the words *Mount Everest*.

Geoterm and Symbol	Definition	Sentence
acclimatize		
carrying capacity		
exposure		
World Heritage site		

29.3 From Lukla to Base Camp

1. On the map, color the route from Lukla to Base Camp. Also fill in the elevations.

   Starting elevation: _____ feet

   Ending elevation: _____ feet

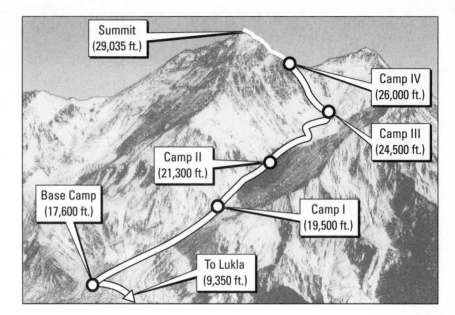

2. Why is it important for climbers to acclimatize?

3. What positive effects have climbing expeditions and tourism had on Nepal? What negative effects have they had?

4. Compare what you just read to your classroom experience.
   List at least two similarities and two differences.

Similarities	Differences

29.4 From Base Camp to Camp I

1. Color the route from Base Camp to Camp I, and fill in the elevations.

    Starting elevation: _____ feet

    Ending elevation: _____ feet

2. Why is the Khumbu Icefall the most dangerous part of the climb up Everest?

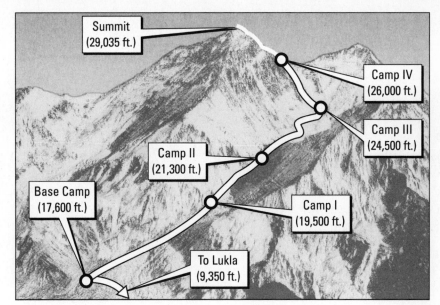

3. What role do Sherpas play on Everest expeditions?

4. Compare what you just read to your classroom experience. List at least two similarities and two differences.

Similarities	Differences

29.5 From Camp I to Camp IV

1. Color the route from Camp I to Camp IV, and fill in the elevations.

   Starting elevation: _____ feet

   Ending elevation: _____ feet

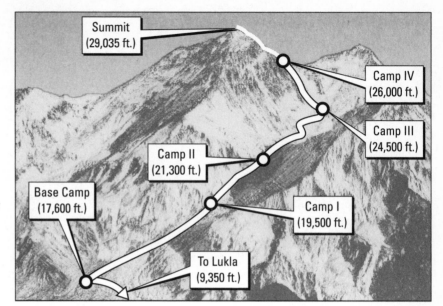

2. Describe how the physical geography changes from Camp I to Camp IV.

3. What is being done to clean up Mount Everest?

4. Compare what you just read to your classroom experience. List at least two similarities and two differences.

Similarities	Differences

29.6 From Camp IV to Summit

1. Color the route from Camp IV to the summit, and fill in the elevations.

   Starting elevation: _____ feet

   Ending elevation: _____ feet

2. What difficulties do climbers face in trying to reach the summit?

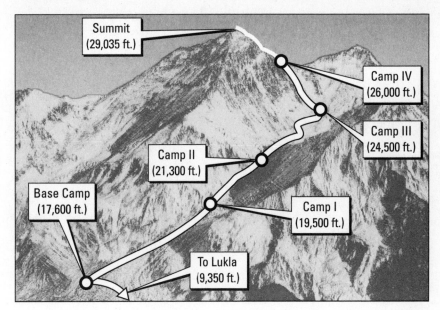

Summit (29,035 ft.)

Camp IV (26,000 ft.)

Camp III (24,500 ft.)

Camp II (21,300 ft.)

Base Camp (17,600 ft.)

Camp I (19,500 ft.)

To Lukla (9,350 ft.)

3. Over the years, how have climbers sought new challenges?

4. Compare what you just read to your classroom experience. List at least two similarities and two differences.

Similarities	Differences

Suppose you have just successfully climbed to Mount Everest's summit. Reflect on your climb by completing four journal entries. Follow these steps:

- For each section of your climb, write a short paragraph describing your experience.

- Draw a sketch to illustrate each journal entry. Add a short caption to each sketch. Each caption should describe the sketch and how it relates to that part of the climb.

- Include these Geoterms at least once in your entries: *acclimatize, carrying capacity, exposure, World Heritage site.*

- Use correct grammar and spelling.

- Add clever and creative touches to make your journal entries realistic.

From Lukla to Base Camp

From Base Camp to Camp I

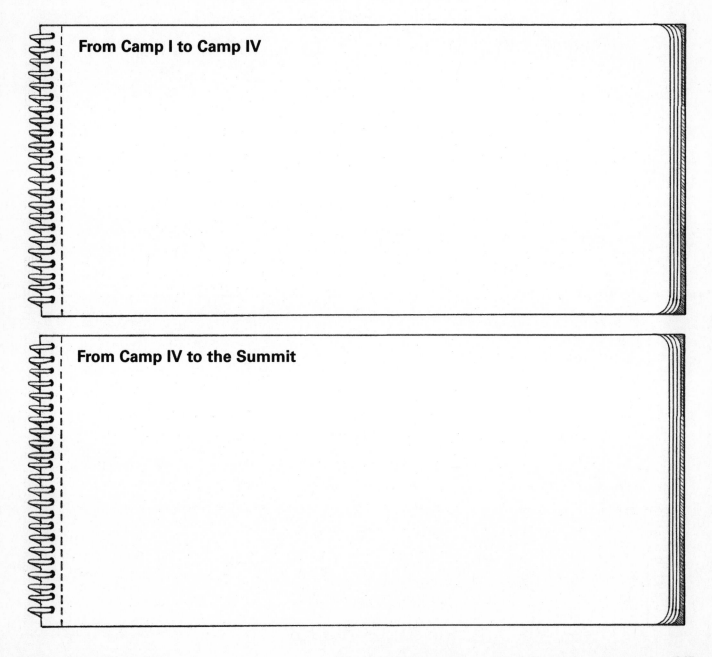

From Camp I to Camp IV

From Camp IV to the Summit

Read Sections 30.1 and 30.2. Then create an illustrated dictionary of the Geoterms by completing these tasks:

- Create a symbol or an illustration to represent each term.
- Write a definition of each term in your own words.
- Write a sentence that includes the term and the word *China*.

Geoterm and Symbol	Definition	Sentence
doubling time		
famine		
rate of natural increase		
zero population growth		

30.3 Plan One: Slow Population Growth

Read Section 30.3. Then complete the steps below.

Step 1: On the graph, draw a vertical line for the year the one-child policy began. Label the line with the policy and the year.

Step 2: Answer these questions:

- What was the Great Leap Forward? What challenges did it create for China?

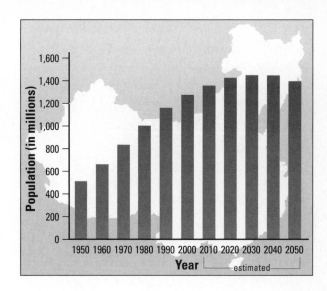

- How does the one-child policy try to address the challenges created by China's large and growing population?

Step 3: Evaluate the impact of the one-child policy on China. List at least two benefits and two costs below.

Benefits of the One-Child Policy	Costs of the One-Child Policy

Step 4: Discuss the question below with your group. Then mark an X along the spectrum to show your group's decision. Be ready to defend your placement by explaining the benefits and costs of the one-child policy.

Critical Thinking Question A: As a demographer, how strongly would you recommend the use of the one-child policy to meet the challenges created by a large and growing population? What evidence would you use to support your recommendation?

Definitely Not
Recommended   Strongly
                                                              Recommended

30.4 Plan Two: Provide More Clean Energy

Read Section 30.4. Then complete the steps below.

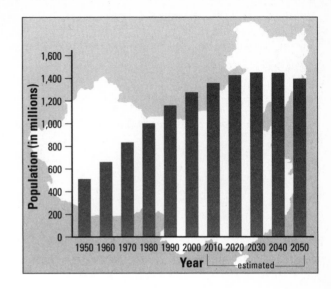

Step 1: On the graph, draw a vertical line for the year the Three Gorges Dam project began. Label the line with the project and the year.

Step 2: Answer these questions:

• What challenges does China face in supplying energy to its population?

• How is the Three Gorges Dam intended to help China address those challenges?

Step 3: Evaluate the impact of the Three Gorges Dam on China. List at least two benefits and two costs below.

Benefits of the Three Gorges Dam	Costs of the Three Gorges Dam

Step 4: Discuss the question below with your group. Then mark an X along the spectrum to show your group's decision. Be ready to defend your placement by explaining the benefits and costs of the Three Gorges Dam.

Critical Thinking Question B: As a demographer, how strongly would you recommend the building of a large hydroelectric dam to meet the challenges created by a large and growing population? What evidence would you use to support your recommendation?

Definitely Not Recommended |————————|————————|————————|————————| **Strongly Recommended**

30.5 Plan Three: Promote Economic Growth

Read Section 30.5. Then complete the steps below.

Step 1: On the graph, draw a vertical line for the year that the first special economic zones were created. Label the line with the policy and the year.

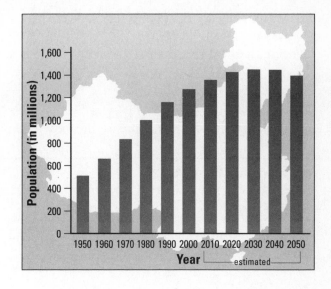

Step 2: Answer these questions:

• How did China's economy work under Mao Zedong?

• How were the special economic zones intended to help China's economy?

Step 3: Evaluate the impact of special economic zones on China. List at least two benefits and two costs below.

Benefits of the SEZs	Costs of the SEZs

Step 4: Discuss the question below with your group. Then mark an X along the spectrum to show your group's decision. Be ready to defend your placement by explaining the benefits and costs of special economic zones.

Critical Thinking Question C: As a demographer, how strongly would you recommend the creation of special economic zones to meet the challenges created by a large and growing population? What evidence would you use to support your recommendation?

Definitely Not Recommended |———|———|———|———| **Strongly Recommended**

Step 1: Use the Global Databank to identify at least five countries with large and rapidly growing populations. A large population is 50 million people or more. A rapidly growing population has a rate of natural increase of 2% or higher. On the world map, label each country with its name, population, and rate of natural increase.

Step 2: Select one of the countries you identified. Create a demographic profile of the country by completing the table below. Add data for China and the world for comparison. Use the Global Databank to help you.

Statistic	Country: _____	China
Population		
Annual Population Growth from Births and Deaths		
Life Expectancy		
Gross Domestic Product (per capita)		
Doctors (per 1,000 people)		
Televisions (per 1,000 people)		
Internet Use (per 1,000 people)		

Step 3: Answer these questions:

- How might the large and rapidly growing population of the country you chose create challenges?

- Describe what you think would be the most effective plan for meeting these challenges.

- Explain why you think your plan would be effective.

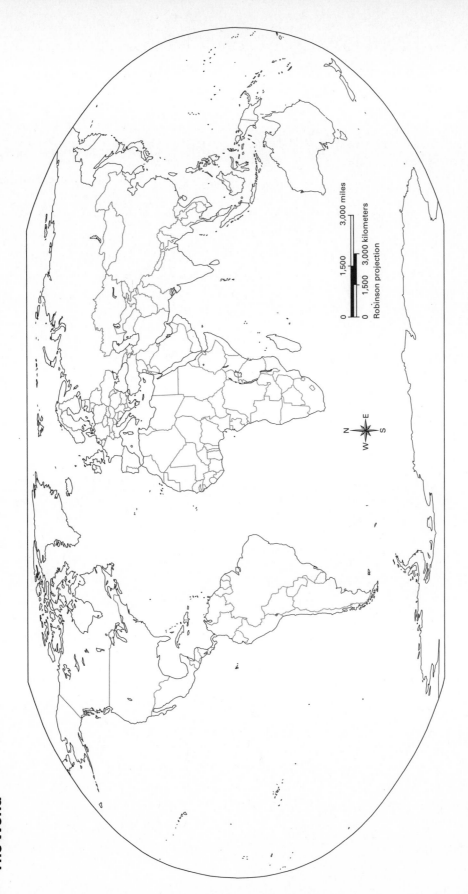

The World

3,000 miles

1,500

0

3,000 kilometers

1,500

0

Robinson projection

N
W E
S

1. Examine the map of Japan your teacher has projected. With a partner, list five facts about Japan that can be determined from the map.

   Fact 1:

   Fact 2:

   Fact 3:

   Fact 4:

   Fact 5:

2. Fill in the map to show where Japan's mountains and lowlands are located. Use the symbols from the key.

3. Look again at the projected map of Japan. On the map above, mark five X's where you think Japan's five largest cities might be located. Give two reasons why you chose those locations.

   Reason 1:

   Reason 2:

As you read Sections 31.1 and 31.2, compile an illustrated dictionary of the Geoterms by completing these tasks:

- Create a symbol or an illustration to represent each term.
- Write a definition of each term in your own words.
- Write a sentence that includes the term and the word *Japan*.

Geoterm and Symbol	Definition	Sentence
arable land		
arithmetic population density		
physiologic population density		
population distribution		

After reading each of Sections 31.3 to 31.6, complete the corresponding questions.

31.3 How Population Density Affects Transportation

1. How does Japan's high population density affect transportation?
   Read the three statements below. One of them is false. Circle the two you think are true.

   - The average employee in Tokyo commutes (travels) 90 minutes to work.
   - No car can be registered in Tokyo without proof that the owner has a place to park it.
   - The Japanese train and subway system is so advanced that the Japanese buy fewer cars today than in 1960.

2. Read Section 31.3. Put a check mark next to each true statement above.

3. Write a summary of the ways population density affects transportation in Japan. Include at least three details from the reading.

31.4 How Population Density Affects Housing

1. How does Japan's high population density affect housing?
   Read the three statements below. One of them is false. Circle the two you think are true.

   - The average home in Japan is smaller than the average home in the United States.
   - Space limitations have not changed family life in Japan.
   - Many Japanese homes do not have separate bedrooms.

2. Read Section 31.4. Put a check mark next to each true statement above.

3. Write a summary of the ways population density affects housing in Japan. Include at least three details from the reading.

31.5 How Population Density Affects Land Use

1. How does Japan's high population density affect the ways land is used in Japan?
   Read the three statements below. One of them is false. Circle the two you think are true.

   - The Japanese have always built very tall buildings because of limited land.
   - The Japanese grow rice on terraces cut into steep mountainsides.
   - The Japanese have built underground parks and zoos.

   2. Read Section 31.5. Put a check mark next to each true statement above.

   3. Write a summary of the ways population density affects land use in Japan.
      Include at least three details from the reading.

31.6 How Population Density Affects Health

1. How does Japan's high population density affect the environment and people's health?
   Read the three statements below. One of them is false. Circle the two you think are true.

   - Because of crowding in Japan, the Japanese live shorter lives than most people in the world.
   - Some Japanese wear face masks to avoid making others ill.
   - The Japanese recycle cookie wrappers to reduce trash.

2. Read Section 31.6. Put a check mark next to each true statement above.

3. Write a summary of the ways population density affects the environment and health in Japan.
   Include at least three details from the reading.

Conduct a study of how population density affects life in your state and community.

1. Draw a map of your state.

2. Look at the U.S. population density map below. Shade in the most densely populated areas on the map of your state.

3. Use an atlas to find the five largest cities in your state. Label them on your state map.

4. Shade your map to show the population density of the area where you live, if you didn't shade it in Step 2.

5. Somewhere on your map, draw two ways that you believe population density affects life in your state. Then draw two ways that it affects life in your neighborhood. Write a caption for each of your drawings.

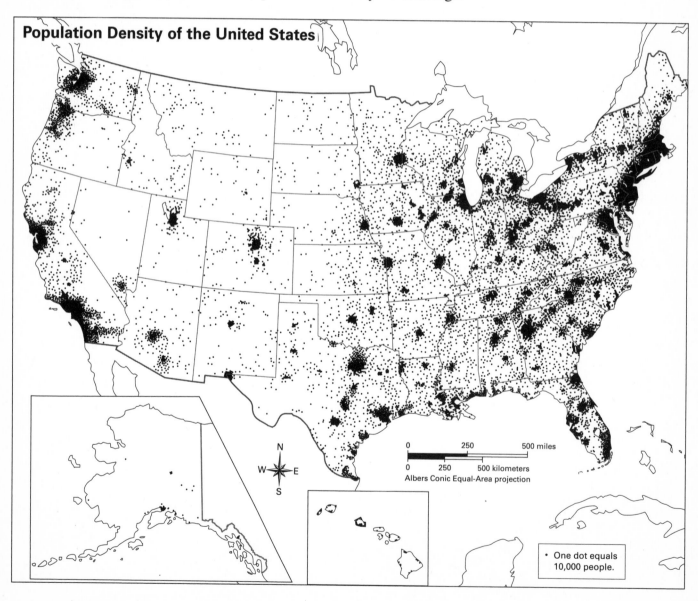

Population Density of the United States

0   250   500 miles

0   250   500 kilometers

Albers Conic Equal-Area projection

N
W E
S

• One dot equals 10,000 people.

Step 1: Your teacher will start a timer. With a partner, inspect the labels on your clothes and other items (backpacks, watches, and so on). In the table below, list each item and the country where it was made. Do this for as many items as you can.

Step 2: Your teacher will stop the timer and then ask you to state an item and a country from your list.

Item	Country

Read Sections 32.1 and 32.2. Then create an illustrated dictionary of the Geoterms by completing these tasks:

- Create a symbol or an illustration to represent each term.
- Write a definition of each term in your own words.
- Write a sentence that includes the term and the word *Asia*.

Geoterm and Symbol	Definition	Sentence
economic interdependence		
free trade		
globalization		
multinational corporation		

Read each section, and complete
the corresponding notes.

32.3 Designing a Global Sneaker

1. On the map, draw a blue dot
   in each country involved in this step
   of producing a global sneaker.

2. List three ways the design of sneakers
   has changed since
   the 1950s.

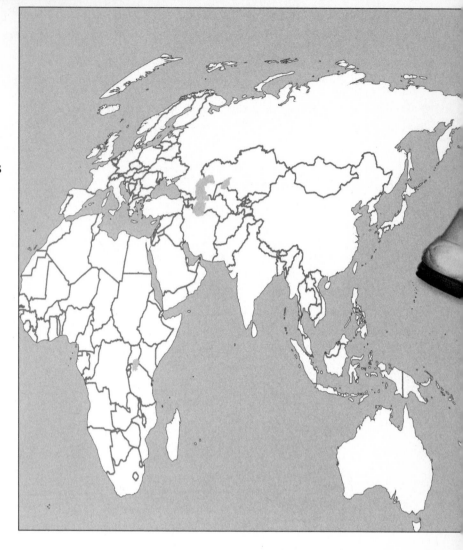

32.4 Locating Global Sneaker Materials

1. On the map, draw a red dot in each country involved in this step of producing a global sneaker.

2. What are the three parts of the sneaker? What materials is each part made of?

3. List a reason why each sneaker material might come from the locations listed.

   • leather from Texas and Venezuela:

   • foam padding from Saudi Arabia:

   • synthetic rubber from Taiwan:

32.5 Manufacturing the Global Sneaker

1. On the map, draw a green dot in each country currently involved in this step of producing a global sneaker.

2. Where were sneakers manufactured until the 1960s? What changes occurred in the 1970s that caused sneaker companies to no longer make shoes at home?

3. List three reasons sneaker companies moved their production offshore to Asian countries.

32.6 Distributing the Global Sneaker

1. On the map, draw a typical sneaker distribution route from Asia to your state.

2. What three modes of transportation are used to move sneakers from Asia to stores in the United States? How is each mode used?

3. What are three advantages of using freight containers to transport products?

Step 1: Gather 20 different items at home. In the table, list each item and the country where it was made.

Item	Country

Step 2: Create a choropleth map of the items on your list. Count the number of items from each country you listed. Shade each country on the map using these colors:

- 1 or 2 items: yellow
- 3 or 4 items: orange
- 5 or more items: blue

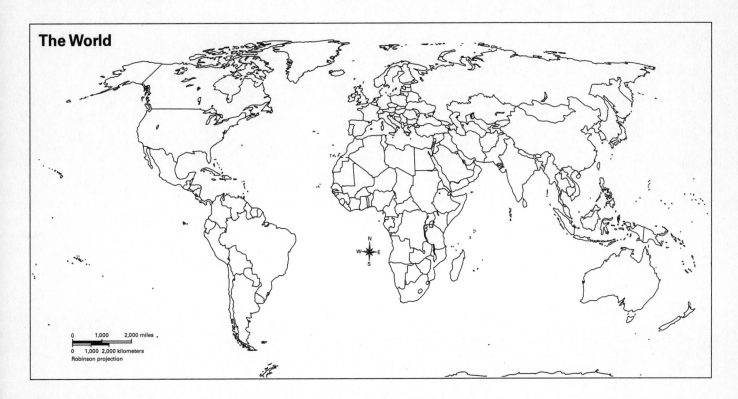

The World

0   1,000   2,000 miles
0   1,000 2,000 kilometers
Robinson projection

Step 3: Analyze the colors on your map. Create two "Why?" or "Where?" questions that relate to it. Write the questions and their answers on another sheet of paper.

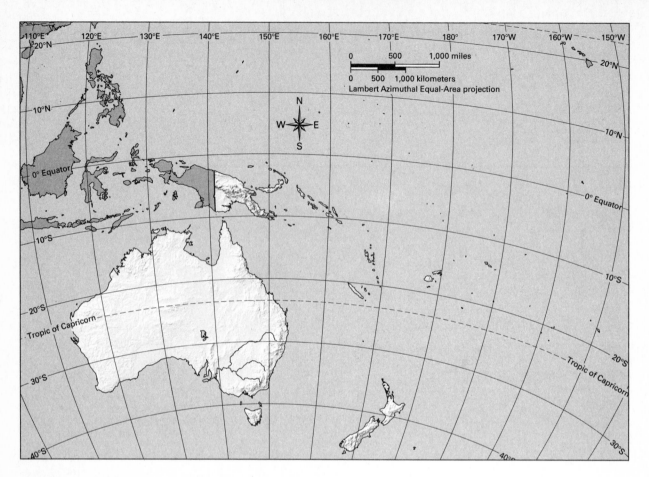

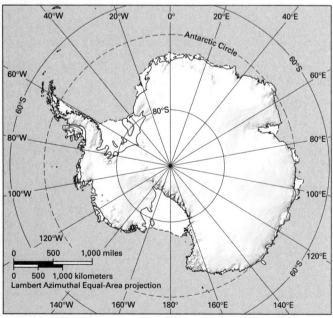

Physical Features of Oceania and Antarctica

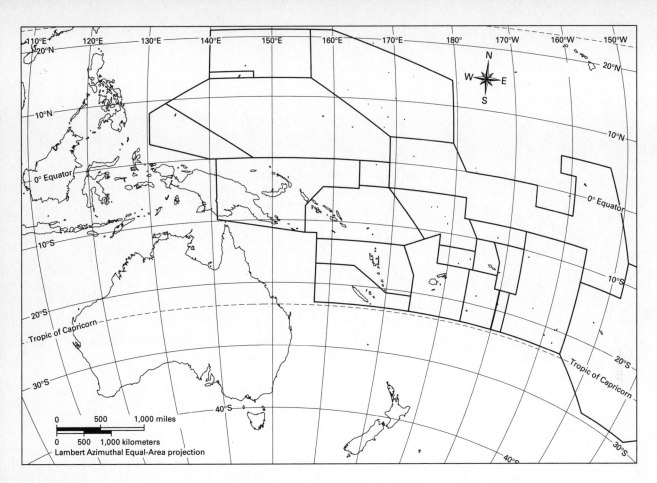

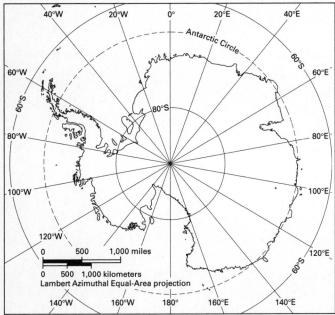

Political Boundaries of Oceania and Antarctica

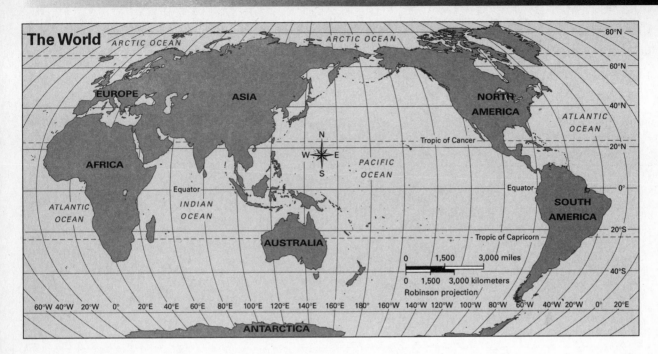

1. How might you describe the location of Australia?

2. Define the terms *absolute location* and *relative location*.
   (**Hint:** If you need help, see the Geoterms in Chapter 1.)

   absolute location:

   relative location:

   In your answer to Question 1, put an *A* next to any examples of
   absolute location. Put an *R* next to any examples of relative location.

3. What are some ways that Australia's location might shape life in
   that country?

Read Sections 33.1 and 33.2. Then create an illustrated dictionary of
the Geoterms by completing these tasks:

- Create a symbol or an illustration to represent each term.
- Write a definition of each term in your own words.
- Write a sentence that includes the term and the word *Australia*.

Geoterm and Symbol	Definition	Sentence
continental drift theory		
endangered species		
exotic species		
native species		
threatened species		

Complete the matching section of Reading Notes for each placard you analyze.

33.3 A Land Far from Great Britain
Transparency: British Influences in Australia

1. Write a possible answer to this question: *Great Britain has had an influence on life in Australia. How do you think Australia's location may have played a role in this?*

2. Read Section 33.3. Use what you learn to revise your answer.

3. Finish this statement: *Relative/absolute location (circle one) is more responsible for shaping British influences on Australia because*

33.4 New Relationships with Near Neighbors
Placard 33A: Immigrants to Australia

1. Write a possible answer to this question: *How do you think Australia's location plays a role in shaping who comes to live there?*

2. Read Section 33.4. Use what you learn to revise your answer.

3. Finish this statement: *Relative/absolute location (circle one) is more responsible for shaping who comes to live in Australia because*

33.5 Australia's Reversed Seasons
Placard 33B: Seasons in Australia

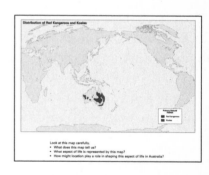

1. Write a possible answer to these questions: *How do you think Australia's location plays a role in shaping its seasons? How might Australia benefit from its seasons?*

2. Read Section 33.5. Use what you learn to revise your answer.

3. Finish this statement: *Relative/absolute location (circle one) is more responsible for shaping seasons in Australia because*

33.6 Australia's Amazing Wildlife
Placard 33C: Wildlife in Australia

1. Write a possible answer to this question: *What role do you think Australia's location has played in shaping the kinds of wildlife found there?*

2. Read Section 33.6. Use what you learn to revise your answer.

3. Finish this statement: *Relative/absolute location (circle one) is more responsible for shaping the kinds of wildlife found in Australia because*

33.7 Living Under an Ozone Hole
Placard 33D: The Sun in Australia

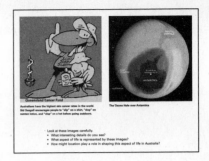

1. Write a possible answer to this question: *How do you think Australia's location impacts the effects of the sun on the people who live there?*

2. Read Section 33.7. Use what you learn to revise your answer.

3. Finish this statement: *Relative/absolute location (circle one) is more responsible for impacting the sun's effect on the people of Australia because*

33.8 Australia's Night Sky
Placard 33E: The Night Sky in Australia

1. Write a possible answer to this question: *How do you think Australia's location affects its view of the night sky?*

2. Read Section 33.8. Use what you learn to revise your answer.

3. Finish this statement: *Relative/absolute location (circle one) is more responsible for shaping Australia's view of the night sky because*

Location, Location, Location!

How does the location of your community shape life where you live? Think of the various aspects of life in Australia that are shaped by its location. How are these same aspects of life in your community or state affected by your location?

Step 1: Draw a dot on the map to show the location of your town or city.

Step 2: Use an atlas or the U.S. map in your book to find the absolute location (latitude and longitude coordinates) of your city or town. Write this on your map.

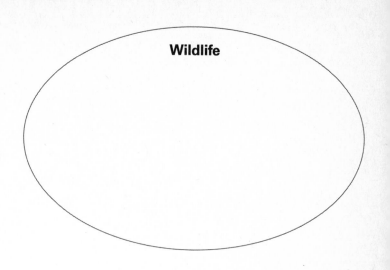

Wildlife

The Night Sky

Step 3: How does location shape life in your city or town? Choose *three* of the five aspects in the ovals on these two pages. In each of those three ovals, write *at least one fact* about how location shapes that aspect. For example, you might research one native species in your area. Under "Wildlife," you would explain why that native species is found near your community.

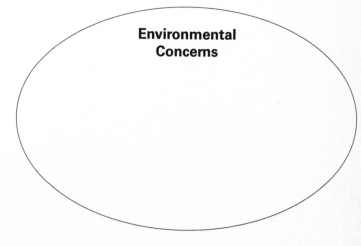

Environmental Concerns

Migration

Seasons and Climate

Look at the satellite image your teacher has projected. With your partner, answer these questions:

- What is the large blue area? What do you think the green and brown dots in the blue area are?

- What islands, countries, or continents do you see?

- What are some ways these islands might be similar to one another?

- What are some ways these islands might be different from one another?

- How do you think your daily routine might be different if you lived on one of these islands?

Read Sections 34.1 and 34.2. Then create an illustrated dictionary of the
Geoterms by completing these tasks:

- Create a symbol or an illustration to represent each term.
- Write a definition of each term in your own words.
- Write a sentence that includes the term and the word *life*.

Geoterm and Symbol	Definition	Sentence
atoll		
continental island		
lagoon		
volcanic island		

34.3 The Ocean Shapes Life in the Pacific

Read Section 34.3, and complete the notes below.

- Around the map, write two facts to explain how ocean surface currents work. Use a line to connect each fact to the appropriate part of the map. An example is done for you.

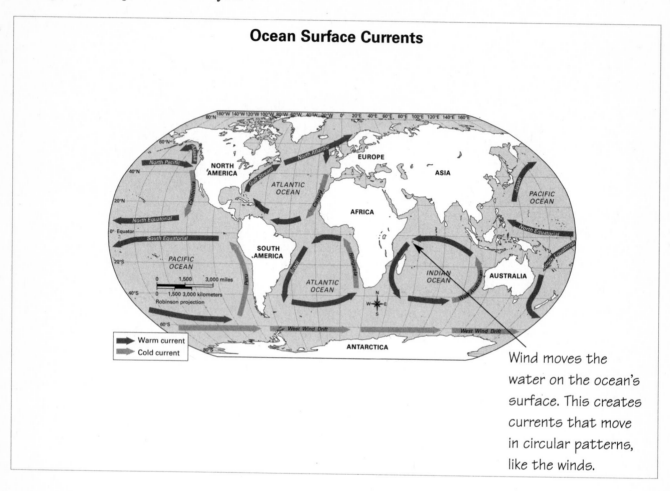

Ocean Surface Currents

Wind moves the water on the ocean's surface. This creates currents that move in circular patterns, like the winds.

- Explain why islands in the Pacific have warm temperatures and lots of rain.

- In the space below, quickly sketch and label four resources found in the Pacific.

34.4 Life on a Continental Island: New Zealand

Step 1: Examine the continental island maps your class created. Take notes below based on what you learn from the maps.

Step 2: Read Section 34.4. Use what you learned in both Sections 34.2 and 34.4 to correct and add to your notes below.

- Around the drawing of a continental island, write two facts about this type of island. Draw a line from each fact to an appropriate part of the island. Add to the drawing if it helps illustrate your facts. An example is done for you.

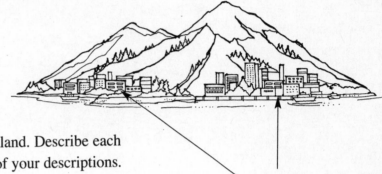

Large cities can usually be found on continental islands.

- Listed below are four features of New Zealand. Describe each feature. Include at least two facts in each of your descriptions.

physical features:

climate:

economy:

human adaptations:

- Which features make New Zealand a classic continental island?

34.5 Life on a Volcanic Island: Tahiti

Step 1: Examine the volcanic island maps your class created. Take notes below based on what you learn from the maps.

Step 2: Read Section 34.5. Use what you learned in both Sections 34.2 and 34.5 to correct and add to your notes below.

- Around the drawing of a volcanic island, write two facts about this type of island. Draw a line from each fact to an appropriate part of the island. Add to the drawing if it helps illustrate your facts. An example is done for you.

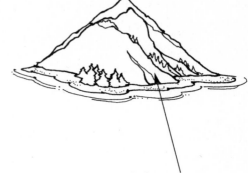

Volcanic islands are created when volcanoes break through the ocean floor. Lava and ash build up on the ocean floor, rising to above sea level.

- Include at least two facts in each of your descriptions.

  physical features:

  climate:

  economy:

  human adaptations:

- What features make Tahiti a classic volcanic island?

34.6 Life on an Atoll: Kwajalein Island

Step 1: Examine the atoll maps your class created. Take notes below based on what you learn from the maps.

Step 2: Read Section 34.6. Use what you learned in both Sections 34.2 and 34.6 to correct and add to your notes below.

- Around the drawing of an atoll, write two facts about this type of island. Draw a line from each fact to an appropriate part of the island. Add to the drawing if it helps illustrate your facts. An example is done for you.

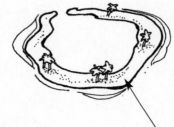

Atolls have very low elevations.

- Listed below are four features of Kwajalein Island. Describe each feature. Include at least two facts in each of your descriptions.

physical features:

climate:

economy:

human adaptations:

- What features makes Kwajalein Atoll a classic atoll?

You have learned about continental islands, volcanic islands, and atolls. What are the differences among these three types of islands? What are the similarities? Complete the Venn diagram below to show your ideas.

- Find the part of each circle that does not overlap with another. In each of these, list two characteristics about that island type that are not shared by the other two.
- Find the part of each circle that overlaps one other island type. In each, list one characteristic shared by those two island types but not by the third type.
- Find the space shared by all three circles. In it, list *three* characteristics shared by all three island types.

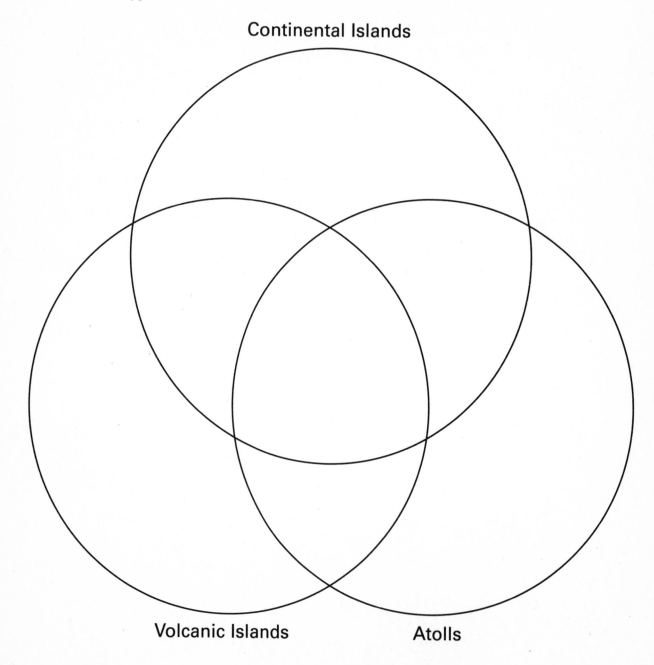

Continental Islands

Volcanic Islands   Atolls

Antarctica is a place of unique and extreme characteristics. But just *how* unique and extreme? Read each statement below. Circle whether you believe each one is a fact or an exaggeration.

- The ice sheets that cover Antarctica average one and a half miles in thickness. The thickest ice is almost three miles thick.

  Fact   **Exaggeration**

- If Antarctica's ice sheets melted, the world's oceans would rise by 200 feet.

  Fact   **Exaggeration**

- Most of Antarctica is a desert. The annual precipitation over Antarctica is less than 2 inches.

  Fact   **Exaggeration**

- From November to February, it almost never gets dark in Antarctica.

  Fact   **Exaggeration**

- Antarctica's largest land predator is a mite. It weighs about the same as two grains of table salt.

  Fact   **Exaggeration**

- The lowest temperature ever recorded on Earth, ⁻128°F, was in Antarctica.

  Fact   **Exaggeration**

- At the beginning of winter, the Antarctic Sea freezes by around 40,000 square miles *per day*, eventually doubling the size of Antarctica.

  Fact   **Exaggeration**

- In 2000, an iceberg broke free from Antarctica. It measured 183 miles long and 23 miles wide—approximately the size of the state of Connecticut.

  Fact   **Exaggeration**

Read Sections 35.1 and 35.2. Then create an illustrated dictionary of
the Geoterms by completing these tasks:

- Create a symbol or an illustration to represent each term.
- Write a definition of each term in your own words.
- Write a sentence that includes the term and the word *Antarctica*.

Geoterm and Symbol	Definition	Sentence
biome		
global warming		
greenhouse effect		
ice shelf		

35.3 The Theory of Global Warming

What three key ideas is the theory of global warming based on?

1.

2.

3.

Fill in the five missing pieces on the diagram of the greenhouse effect.

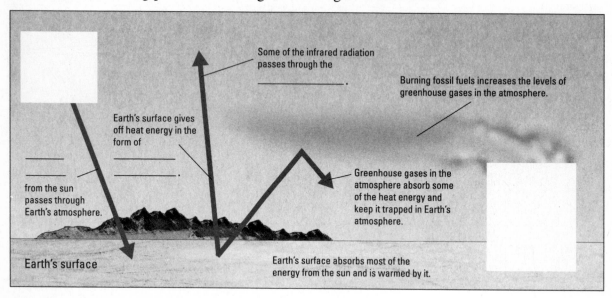

Some of the infrared radiation passes through the

_____ .

Burning fossil fuels increases the levels of greenhouse gases in the atmosphere.

Earth's surface gives off heat energy in the form of

_____

_____ .

_____

from the sun passes through Earth's atmosphere.

Greenhouse gases in the atmosphere absorb some of the heat energy and keep it trapped in Earth's atmosphere.

Earth's surface

Earth's surface absorbs most of the energy from the sun and is warmed by it.

In the first column of the table, list a reason to support each of the three key ideas of the global warming theory. In the second column, list a reason to doubt each key idea.

 35.4 Support for the Global Warming Theory

 35.5 Doubts About the Global Warming Theory

Follow the directions at Amundsen-Scott Station to complete the Reading
Notes below.

35.6 Studying Temperatures in Antarctica

Complete the temperature graph for Amundsen-Scott Station.

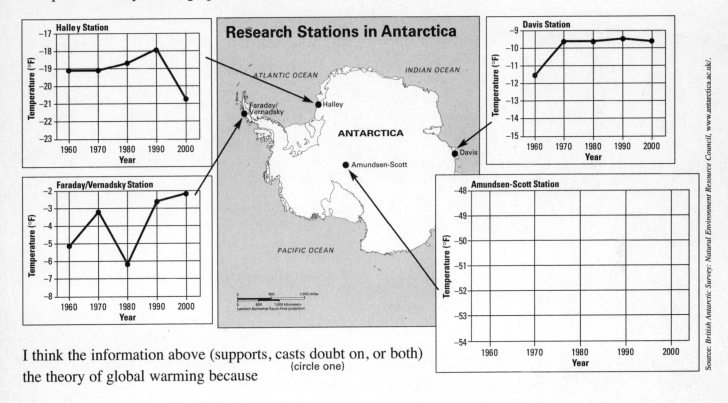

I think the information above (supports, casts doubt on, or both)
the theory of global warming because
(circle one)

In the first column, write arguments that a supporter of the global warming
theory might make. In the second column, write arguments that a doubter
of the theory might make.

 **Geographer Who Supports
the Theory of Global Warming**

 **Geographer Who Doubts
the Theory of Global Warming**

Follow the directions at Rothera Station to complete the Reading
Notes below.

35.7 Studying Ice Shelves in Antarctica

Calculate how much ice was lost from the Larsen Ice Shelf in 2002 by
filling in the blanks below.

Larsen Ice Shelf,
January 31, 2002

Larsen Ice Shelf,
March 5, 2002

A. Total area of Larsen Ice Shelf on January 31, 2002:
    2,749 square miles

B. _____ x 100 square miles = _____ square miles
   (number of *fully*
   colored squares)   +

C. _____ x 50 square miles = _____ square miles
   (number of *partially*
   colored squares)

D. Total area of ice lost between January 31 and March 5, 2002:
    _____ square miles (Add the answers to B and C.)

E. Percentage of ice lost between January 31 and March 5, 2002: _____ %
   (Divide the answer to D by the answer to A. Multiply the result by 100 to turn
   the decimal into a percent.)

I think the information above (supports, casts doubt on, or both)
the theory of global warming because   (circle one)

In the first column, write arguments that a supporter of the global warming
theory might make. In the second column, write arguments that a doubter
of the theory might make.

 **Geographer Who Supports
the Theory of Global Warming**

 **Geographer Who Doubts
the Theory of Global Warming**

Follow the directions at Palmer Station to complete the Reading
Notes below.

35.8 Studying Penguins in Antarctica

Calculate the change in the number of breeding pairs of Adelie
penguins by filling in the blanks below.

A. Total number of breeding pairs, 1975: 16,000

B. Number of breeding pairs in *your* colony, present: _____

C. Number of breeding pairs in other colonies, present: 4,960

D. Total number of breeding pairs, present: _____
(Add the answers to B and C.)

E. Total change in the number of breeding pairs: _____
(Subtract the answer to A from the answer to D.)

F. Percent change in the number of breeding pairs: _____%
(Divide the answer to E by the answer to A. Multiply the result by 100 to turn
the decimal into a percent.)

I think the information above (supports, casts doubt on, or both)
the theory of global warming because   (circle one)

In the first column, write arguments that a supporter of the global warming
theory might make. In the second column, write arguments that a doubter
of the theory might make.

**Geographer Who Supports
the Theory of Global Warming**

**Geographer Who Doubts
the Theory of Global Warming**

Credits